"Dr. Osborn uses his skills as a historian and OCD expert to provide the first comprehensive psychiatric study of Martin Luther since Erik Erikson's Young Man Luther. Rather than leaning on outdated psychoanalytic concepts, Osborn employs modern psychiatric diagnostic criteria to demonstrate clearly and irrefutably that Luther suffered from clinical obsessions and compulsions during his early years. This is an important book for historians, clinicians, and anxiety sufferers alike."
— **Harold G. Koenig**, M.D., Professor of Psychiatry and Behavioral Sciences, Associate Professor of Medicine, and Director, Center for Spirituality, Theology and Health, at Duke University Medical Center

"Dr. Osborn brings the lens of modern psychiatry to the life experience of Martin Luther, demonstrating the role of obsessive-compulsive symptoms in his beliefs, thinking, and scholarly works."
— **Laura Roberts**, MD, MA, Chairman, Department of Psychiatry and Behavioral Sciences, and Katharine Dexter McCormick and Stanley McCormick Memorial Professor, Stanford University School of Medicine. Editor-in-Chief, Books, American Psychiatric Association Publishing

"Part history, part religion, part OCD, this book is a fascinating read about one of the most influential thinkers in recorded history."
— **Patrick B. McGrath**, Ph.D., Chief Clinical Officer, NOCD, and member, Scientific and Clinical Advisory Boards, International OCD Foundation

"This book should be read by both believers and nonbelievers because it shows how the limitations of one's personality can contribute to the genius of one's being... His book is scholarly, yet reads like a novel."
   — **Sally K. Severino,** M.D. Professor Emeritus of Psychiatry, University of New Mexico, and past president of the American College of Psychoanalysts

"An essential read for Christians who are experiencing OCD."
   — **Cherry Pedrick,** coauthor of *The OCD Workbook* and *Loving Someone with OCD*

"I recommend this book to theologians, historians, mental health professionals, individuals with OCD, and all who have grappled with religious doubt."
   — **C. Alec Pollard,** Ph.D., Founding Director, Center for OCD & Anxiety-Related Disorders, Saint Louis Behavioral Medicine Institute, and Professor Emeritus of Family and Community Medicine, Saint Louis University School of Medicine

Martin Luther's
Obsessive-Compulsive Disorder

Also by Ian Osborn, MD

Can Christianity Cure Obsessive-Compulsive Disorder?: A Psychiatrist Explores the Role of Faith in Treatment (2008, Brazos Press)

Tormenting Thoughts and Secret Rituals: The Hidden Epidemic of Obsessive-Compulsive Disorder (1998, Pantheon)

Martin Luther's Obsessive-Compulsive Disorder

How the Great Reformer Cured OCD and What He Learned

IAN OSBORN, MD

OCD Resources Publishing
State College, PA

Martin Luther's Obsessive-Compulsive Disorder:
How the Great Reformer Cured OCD and What He Learned
© 2023, Ian Osborn, MD. All rights reserved.
Published by OCD Resources Publishing, State College, PA

ISBN: 979-8-9876652-0-6 (print)
ISBN: 979-8-9876652-1-3 (eBook)
Library of Congress Control Number: 2023904352

Publication managed by AuthorImprints.com

CONTENTS

Chapter *1*

INTRODUCTION

*M*artin Luther is among the most influential religious thinkers of all time. As a measure of his impact, he is said to have had more books and articles written about him than any other Christian figure.[1] More than a billion present-day Protestant Christians owe their form of worship to him. Impressively, the Roman Catholic Church, his old antagonist, recently acknowledged Luther's greatness as a reformer, and issued a stamp in his honor.

Luther's fame rests primarily on the fact that he started and led the sixteenth-century Protestant Reformation, a massive revolt against the scandal-plagued Roman Catholic Church of his time that reshaped the religious course of the Western world. Luther rebelled primarily because he believed that certain teachings of the church were causing great harm to her members. Most important was the issue of how a person pleases God and becomes "righteous."

Catholic doctrine has always stressed that right standing with God depends in part on following God's commands and performing good works, such as charitable acts. After prolonged study and intense internal struggle, Luther came to a much different view: Righteousness depends completely on God's grace and a person's faith. This new perspective flew in the face of traditional teachings. As put by Harvard historian Heiko Oberman, "Luther's discovery rent the very fabric of Christian ethics. Reward and merit, so long undisputed as the basic motivation for all human action, were robbed of their efficacy."[2]

A great controversy has existed from Luther's time to the present day over why Luther came to believe so passionately in an idea that seemed extreme. Catholic polemicists argued for centuries that Luther was out of his mind and unable to think clearly. To make their case, they leaned on statements that Luther made about certain tormenting "spiritual trials" he experienced during the years when he developed his reformational beliefs. Luther described them as,

> "Punishments so great and so much like hell that no tongue could adequately express them, no pen could describe them, and one who had not himself experienced them could not believe them .... At such a time God seems terribly angry, and with him the whole creation. At such a time there is no flight, no comfort, within or without, but all things accuse."[3]

Johannes Cochlaeus, a priest and scholar who debated Luther, published an influential biography arguing that Luther was controlled by Satan.[4] This became the Catholic party line. As time passed, defenders of the Catholic faith shifted their emphasis to proving that Luther was insane. One well-respected German priest and theologian wrote that Luther was "so overwhelmed by such a gloomy, depressing state of mind that he developed wildly confused, contradictory and destructive ideas that dominated his whole life and thought." [5] As recently as 1911, a well-known Jesuit scholar wrote that Luther's mental imbalance was so severe that it prevented rational thinking.[6] All the while, Protestant defenders countered just as vigorously that Luther had no significant psychological problems. Like the prophets of the Old Testament, they argued, Luther was simply tested severely.

One hopes psychiatrists brought a degree of clarity to the nature of Luther's agonizing problems. In fact, two respected clinicians wrote books on Luther in the twentieth century, but these only caused more controversy. In 1937, Danish psychiatrist Paul Reiter published a two-volume work[7] on the Great Reformer, diagnosing him with a degenerative disorder of the brain that began in his early twenties and developed into a frank psychosis. In 1958, the esteemed psychoanalyst Erik Erikson published his highly influential book *Young Man Luther*, in which he suggested Luther suffered from a "borderline psychotic state."[8] Yet the conclusions of both biographers were largely dismissed by Luther experts on the basis of inaccuracies in the authors' accounts of Luther's life. Since then, biographers and historians have generally avoided drawing conclusions about Luther's psychiatric diagnosis. Luther's most popular biographer, Roland Bainton, wisely observed in the mid-twentieth century, "The question [of Luther's diagnosis] can be better faced when more data become available."[9]

The data are available now. As a result of fifty years of intensive research into the cause and treatment of psychiatric disorders, we can now understand Luther's terrifying fears in an objective, clinical manner that was not possible even a few decades ago.

This book will demonstrate that, notwithstanding the difficulties involved in attempting to retrospectively diagnose a historical figure, Luther's agonizing spiritual trials represented a case of what psychiatrists today call obsessive-compulsive disorder (OCD). This condition, still much misunderstood by the general public, is a fairly easily recognized and relatively common anxiety syndrome that is marked by intrusive, tormenting thoughts and the repetitive acts that are done to relieve them.

The following chapters will show how Luther cured[10] his disorder through discovering fresh new meanings in biblical texts. Much evidence points to the fact that Luther overcame his torment over a period of approximately six years immediately prior to the Reformation. Remarkably, rather than comforting himself with scripture passages that reassured him of his salvation (e.g., "God will honor me"), Luther focused his attention on texts that aggravated his fears (e.g., "I have done that which is evil"). This is exactly how we treat OCD in the present day. We encourage people to purposefully expose themselves to their most fearful thoughts in a forceful, structured manner. Through the use of this approach, obsessional fears gradually lose their sting. The book will demonstrate how, in a remarkable display of biblical scholarship, determination, and therapeutic intuition, Luther cured his disorder in a manner that would make a modern OCD therapist proud.

But there is more to the story. The book will also suggest that from a strictly clinical point of view (and without denying the possibility of supernatural intervention), it was through curing his spiritual trials that Luther learned his most important lessons about what makes a person righteous in God's eyes. Luther himself tells us,

> "I didn't learn my theology all at once. I had to ponder over it ever more deeply, and my spiritual trials were of help to me in this.... Only spiritual trial teaches what Christ is."[11]

Without the benefit of his obsessional fears, one could argue, the Great Reformer might never have strongly challenged the Roman Catholic Church, nor pursued the Reformation at all.

Chapter **2**

LUTHER'S TIMES: THE RENAISSANCE EPIDEMIC OF RELIGIOUS FEARS

*M*artin Luther lived during the heart of the Renaissance in Western Europe. His contemporaries in the fifteenth and sixteenth centuries included Copernicus, Galileo, Leonardo de Vinci, and Christopher Columbus. The Renaissance is known for its unparalleled scientific, artistic, and humanistic achievements. It is considered the time when medieval civilization gave way to modern ways of thinking.

For the peasants who comprised the vast majority of the population, unfortunately, the Renaissance was notable mainly for personal hardship and social upheaval. Many lived in disease-infested huts, with little to eat. The bubonic plague was making regular rounds, taking down huge swaths of the population. Economic stresses led to bloody uprisings. In an effort to curtail rebellion, governors and authorities across Europe instituted a long list of crimes that were punishable by hanging, beheading, and the "wheel." Death was on peoples' minds to a degree that is hard to imagine today. Many thought the end of the world was near.

The great majority of the 70 million people who lived in Western Europe identified as Roman Catholics, and it is generally agreed that few of them doubted the major tenets of their faith. The stars were moved by angels; even scholars believed in witchcraft. Witch-hunts were common, and nowhere were they more feverishly pursued than in Luther's homeland.[1] The day of judgment was a real time of reckoning, and the prospect of eternal life in heaven loomed large in the minds of many. For them the best antidote to despair of earthly life was looking forward to the next.

But the Church was making this remedy difficult. Committing any one of a catalog of sins could lead the sinner to 10,000 years of suffering in purgatory, or being sent straight to hell. Contemporary artists such as Hieronymus Bosch conjured unimaginably gruesome images of these places of torment. As noted by Father Ladislas Orsy of Georgetown University, an expert in the field of moral theology,

> "With the Renaissance came an inflation of mortal sins to an excess that today we recognize as absurd.... Hell became a greater menace for the Christian community than it ever was in the gospel. Damnation became a close threat hanging over the people."[2]

Before the Late Middle Ages, ordinary Christians had not needed to be concerned about their relationship with God—all church members in good standing could feel secure that they would live eternally in heaven after death. This began to change when a new and progressive philosophy took hold in the Roman Catholic Church, championed by the great thirteenth-century theologian, Saint Thomas Aquinas. The "scholastic" movement emphasized peoples' ability to change their lives for the better through the use of reason. As observed by historian Thomas Tentler,

> "The fundamental assumption became [that] ratio-
> nal man is free and responsible, and he can apply this
> teaching to his life."[3]

This new emphasis on man's ability to reason initiated a strong humanistic movement in the Church, and led to the founding of universities. Regrettably, the new system of thought came to be applied in a particularly zealous manner to peoples' identifying and taking responsibility for their sins.

Moral theology, the branch of Christian thought that deals with peoples' attitudes and behaviors, came to assume a central role in Catholic teachings; and as time passed, moral theologians put ever greater burdens on the faithful. In the Middle Ages, only three sins—murder, adultery, and idolatry—could cause a person to lose salvation; by the end of the Renaissance there were hundreds. In the area of sexual behavior alone, thirteen different types of sinful acts were defined and categorized, and the seriousness of each was further broken down according to the degree of genuine contrition felt by the sinner.

A person's behaviors were not the only cause for concern. Moral theologians also reached the conclusion that thoughts about sinful acts could represent mortal sins. Entertaining the idea to hurt another person, for example, could be as grave a sin as committing the crime. To justify this interpretation, theologians turned to the Bible, quoting for instance the well-known passage where Jesus stressed the harsh verdict that would fall on those who harbored malice toward their brother (Matt. 5:22).

Such a reading represented a radical departure from what had previously been taught.

In view of the increased burdens placed on its flock, the Church saw fit to provide a means of consolation as well. In 1215, Pope Innocent III[4] imposed a new obligation on all church members: They were to sincerely confess their sins to a priest at least once a year. The basic idea behind regular confession was a good one. Since Christians could know and weigh their own sins, the Pope sought to ensure that they had opportunity to receive forgiveness for their failings. In the early centuries of regular confession, however, the practice proved a nightmare for many, as confession too often turned into outright interrogation—a search for sin where none was apparent.

The confessor, who was likened to a physician, was charged with exploring the extent of disease in a person's soul. He was to conduct a detailed inquiry into the nooks and shadows of an individual's conscience. Usually, an inquiry into the presence of one of the seven deadly sins was the starting point. Typically, a serious sin was discovered, perhaps lying or jealousy. Then the confessor would point out the need for suitable penance which, if not accomplished, would leave the person damned. Indeed, one of the stated goals of confession was to provoke an acute sense of fear over the possible loss of salvation. William of Auvergne, author of a well-known thirteenth-century guide for confessors, wrote that in the conduct of confession there was "nothing to fear but the lack of fear."[5]

As confession took shape primarily as an inquisition, many people of tender conscience were driven to agonizing states of anxiety over sins they may have committed. People confessed again and again, adding small details they might have forgotten.

Many confessions, as noted by Tentler, "led to psychological and spiritual disaster."[6]

Largely as a result of these changes in church practices, a great outbreak of religious fears took hold. These were given a special name: scruples, deriving from the Latin scrupulum, meaning a tiny pebble of the sort that can stick in a person's shoe and cause pain and suffering far out of proportion to its size. In the present day, scrupulous usually implies extreme attention to detail. In the Late Middle Ages, however, a scruple came to mean an excessive fear of having sinned. It described the torment of doubt within a person over whether or not they have committed a sinful act. Scruples is one of the terms both Luther and his confessor used to describe his spiritual trials.[7]

Orsy observes that scrupulosity was rarely mentioned in the first five or six centuries of Christian writings; its appearance became commonplace only during the Renaissance.[8] Consistent with this view, Historian J. Jerome, writing in the French review La Vie Spirituelle, suggests that troubling fears about sinfulness did not exist prior to the Late Middle Ages.[9] By the fifteenth century, however, mild cases of scrupulosity were considered entirely normal and large numbers of guilt-ridden Christians suffered desperately. For them, the burden of identifying and attending to their sins proved overwhelming.

In the present day, scrupulosity is considered a subtype of obsessive-compulsive disorder. The Renaissance, it turns out, was a hothouse for the development of OCD. This is not surprising given what researchers have discovered: OCD is triggered specifically when a person feels overwhelmed by the responsibility for preventing harm. In Luther's times, the Catholic church put more responsibility than ever before on the shoulders of believers to ensure their place in heaven. Many could not endure the pressures. (See Appendix A for more about the cause of OCD.)

Chapter *3*

THE SENSITIVITY OF YOUNG MARTIN

*M*artin Luther was born in 1483 in Eisleben, a town of several thousand people in the rugged mountains of eastern Germany. His clan had lived in the area for centuries; like most, they were poor, peasant farmers. By the time of Luther's birth, however, large deposits of copper had been discovered nearby. Mines prospered and created much-needed employment opportunities.

Martin's father, Hans, and his brother, Little Hans, were two of the many who left their family farms to labor in the mines. The Luther men were both tough and rough-edged. Over the years, the brother fared poorly, being arrested regularly for drunken assaults and knife fights. Martin's father, on the other hand, kept out of trouble and flourished. He was hardworking and well respected, becoming a manager of smelters and eventually his district's representative to city council. He liked to have a good time. Luther in his later years remembered with fondness how his father joked and sang after returning home from work and having a few beers.[1]

Martin's mother, Margarete, came from a prosperous local family that probably aided Hans with his career. She was known for her domestic virtues and devout character.[2] She had nine children, only five of whom made it to adulthood, the others succumbing to childhood illnesses and the plague. She was a fervent Roman Catholic, who prayed on her knees with her children every day. Luther remembers her as a tireless worker, scavenging firewood from the forest during times of scarcity. More introverted than Hans, she had a fearful view of the world that was fueled by superstition. She warned Martin to stay away from a neighbor who she thought might be possessed, for example, and believed witches from the forest turned themselves into mice and stole food. Young Martin did not doubt these stories, and throughout his life he remained convinced of the power of witchcraft and magic.

Hans and Margarete were strict disciplinarians. Luther spoke of two harsh punishments he received as a child. "My father," Luther recalls, "once whipped me so that I ran away and felt ugly toward him until he was at pains to win me back." And his mother "for the sake of stealing a nut beat me until the blood flowed."[3] A few psychoanalytically oriented biographers have made much of these two statements, suggesting that Luther's anxieties took root in early life conflicts fueled by distrust of his parents. The strong consensus now, however, is that Luther had a good, even unusually close relationship with both of his parents;[4] and throughout his life he felt a great responsibility to please them.

Young Martin was conscientious and promising. His parents stretched their finances to send him to private school, choosing him from among his siblings. Martin was also prone to worry, especially about the question of whether he would attain life in heaven. A popular illustration in Luther's time showed Christ seated on a rainbow on Judgment Day, oddly aloof and uncaring, with a sword protruding from one ear and a flower from the other, evidently equally ready to offer mercy or condemnation to those who came before him. Luther testified that he was utterly terror-stricken at this sight of Christ the judge. At age fourteen, his attention was riveted by the sight of an emaciated monk, who, it turned out, was a prince who had sacrificed his fortune to live an austere and holy life. Comparing the monk to himself, Martin was gripped by guilt. He "could not look at him without feeling ashamed."[5]

Was there was anything abnormal about Martin Luther's childhood psychological state? Roland Bainton sums up the opinion of the major biographers:

> "There is just one respect in which Luther appears to have been different from other youths of his time, namely, in that he was extraordinarily sensitive."[6]

Despite his sensitivity, however, Martin had no problems successfully traversing adolescence. He was popular with his peers and caused no problems for anyone. He was physically strong and energetic. He became a fine musician, proficient on the lute and a good singer. A fellow student remembered him at age seventeen: "a lively, cheerful fellow ... short, and stockily built, headstrong, with keen, deep-set brown eyes and brown hair."[7]

Martin attended three different schools from age seven to seventeen. The first, a Latin school endowed by the local aristocracy, provided basic teaching in reading, writing, and arithmetic. The second school was part of a monastic community, The Brethren of the Common Life. Intensely pious, it included a focus on the practice of inner spirituality. The last institution was a parish school at which Martin received instruction in the faith. During these years he lived for the most part with relatives or friends near the schools he attended. He proved to be an able but not exceptional student. Nevertheless, at age eighteen, in 1501, Martin moved to the University at Erfurt to study logic, philosophy, and theology. For the first time, he studied Christian teachings in depth; he slowly began to excel. After the first year he ranked thirtieth in a class of fifty-two; by his fourth year he had vaulted to second.[8]

Toward the end of his years in college, just as he was coming into his own as a scholar, significant psychological problems began to surface. Luther remembers that he "continually wandered about sadly because of *Anfechtung*,"[9] the German word he uses throughout his writings to describe a distinct condition of fearfulness and doubt. There being no exact English equivalent, the editors of the American edition of *Luther's Works* render anfechtung (plural form anfechtungen) contextually in various ways, including "grave temptations," "doubt and inner turmoil," and "spiritual trials." Luther often uses anfechtung to describe what psychiatrists today call an obsessional fear.

In response to his fears and doubts, Luther says, "I devoted myself to much reading of the Bible."[10] Not only did he immerse himself in scripture, he began to make lengthy and scrupulous confessions. The German historian Martin Brecht, without a doubt Luther's most-thorough biographer, concludes that in his last year at Erfurt, Luther was "having an inner crisis [and] searching the Bible for an answer to his problems."[11] Was this a clinical case of obsessive-compulsive disorder, or simply a young man embarked on an arduous spiritual quest? In my opinion, Luther's OCD probably started here. Not enough is known about this period of his life, however, to answer the question definitively.

Martin's parents were pushing him to become a lawyer in order to help with official matters in the family's copper smelting business. Martin, a dutiful son, embarked on the study of law at the University of Erfurt in the summer of 1505. After a few weeks, he journeyed home by foot for a visit with his parents. Brecht speculates that he was summoned by his father to talk about his prospects of marriage. Whatever the occasion, on the long walk back to the university, a momentous event occurred.

Near the village of Stotternheim, when he was still six kilometers from Erfurt, a thunderstorm broke out. A lightning bolt struck and knocked Luther to the ground. Filled with terror, he looked up to heaven, and made an impassioned pledge to the patron saint of those threatened with sudden death. He cried out:

"Help me Saint Anne, I will become a monk!"[12]

It was for assurance of his place in heaven that Luther made the fateful promise. He would later explain, "I took the vow for the sake of my salvation ... If I were to enter the monastery, I thought, and serve God in cowl and tonsure, he will reward me and welcome me."[13] In a letter to his father he wrote,

"I did not become a monk of my own free will and desire ... I was walled in by the terror and the agony of sudden death and forced by necessity to take the vow."[14]

Terrified of facing God's judgment, in a flash and apparently without reflection, he cast aside his parents' wishes and completely redirected his life. An extraordinary happening. Had he been considering joining the monastery? He had been growing ever more concerned about the state of his soul, and the curriculum he studied prepared him for theology as well as for law. Perhaps the near-death episode simply wrenched from him a decision that had already been on his mind.

Whatever the particulars, Luther's thunderstorm incident is one of the most famous conversion experiences in the history of the Christian Church, sometimes compared to the Apostle Paul's epiphany on the Damascus road and Augustine's experience in the garden in Milan. A short two weeks later, after gathering his belongings and saying his goodbyes, Martin Luther knocked on the door of the imposing Augustinian monastery in Erfurt.

BECOMING A MONK

There were numerous monasteries in the vicinity of Erfurt, a city of 20,000, and Luther never revealed why he chose the Augustinians. They were a reformed order, one that strictly followed the monastic rules of discipline. This would have appealed to him, as he recognized that his vow to St. Anne required him to make a meaningful self-sacrifice. In addition, the monastery contained a well-known theological school, and he may have seen in it the possibility of furthering his biblical studies.

In Luther's time, becoming a monk was assuming a privileged place in God's kingdom. The great Saint Thomas Aquinas had declared that it brought about a second baptism, restoring the individual to the state of complete innocence. When Luther stepped through the door, he had every reason to believe that his eternal destiny was secure.

Monks withdrew from the world in order to dedicate themselves to God. They maintained silence as much as possible and endured cold, solitude, and hunger so that earthly desires could be subdued. The fifty-two monks of Luther's monastery gathered six times a day and once in the middle of the night to chant the Psalms. They also spent considerable time in private prayer and attended Mass daily. All monks also engaged in physical or intellectual labor. Most were assigned menial tasks, while a smaller number were encouraged to become theologians. The Augustinian Erfurt monastery was especially well-known for developing scholars.

Luther's academic potential was quickly recognized. In order to earn a teaching degree, young monks were usually required to complete a four-year general curriculum, followed by three or more years of intensive theological studies. Yet after only a year and a half, Luther was lecturing on selected topics, and within six years he had received a doctor's degree in theology and became a professor of bible studies.

At first, Luther's stay in the monastery went rather well. He was enthusiastic about his new vocation and felt a sense of peace. Looking back, he observed, "I experienced in myself how tranquil Satan was wont to be in the first years of monkdom."[15] From a psychological perspective, this makes sense. His doubts about salvation would have been relieved by the assurance that as a monk he rested in a privileged place before God. Perhaps even more importantly, the rigorous schedule of the monastery would have curtailed his time for worrying.

By the end of Luther's second year, however, unshakable worries resurfaced. They crystalized in a dramatic event. Luther was chosen to become a priest. This was not unusual, as most monks in his monastery were rewarded with this distinction.

After training and instruction were completed, only one crucial event remained for the new priest: presiding over his first Mass. For the first time, he would meet God face to face as he offered up the body and blood of Christ. It was a solemn, sacramental rite of passage. A celebration typically followed a priest's first Mass, and relatives and friends were invited. Yet Luther felt no joy or satisfaction on this important occasion. Instead, during the Mass he panicked. He later described the event:

> "The first time I read these words in the Canon of the Mass: 'We offer to Thee, the living, the true, and the eternal God,' I was completely stunned, and I shuddered at those words. For I used to think: 'With what impudence I am addressing so great a Majesty, when everybody should be terrified.'"[16]

Fear of God's wrath shook him to the core, becoming close to disabling. He wanted to run from the altar. He requested to be relieved then and there of his duty but was ordered to continue. This unexpected and shattering event signaled the onset of a dozen years of tortuous anxieties centered on his relationship with God.

Luther would live as a monk for a total of fifteen years.[17] These conveniently divide into two distinct time periods that differ significantly as to the nature of the anxieties he suffered. During his early monastery years, from approximately 1505 to 1514, he dreaded that he would fall short in good works and thereby lose his salvation. In his later years, his terrors became even more acute, and he feared God completely abandoned him. Over the course of Luther's years in the monastery, his life situation also underwent a dramatic transformation. Early on, he remained for the most part an unknown monk. After he began his revolution against the Catholic Church in 1517, he quickly gained fame and began a breathtakingly exciting public life.

Regarding Luther's later years in the monastery, a great deal is known. People were writing about him and copying down what he said. He was also publishing his own books and articles, sometimes providing glimpses into his mental state. The situation with the early years, however, is entirely different. We have only some of the lecture notes from his teaching, and his own reminiscences about the time from many years later. His reminiscences, however, were numerous and lucid.

When Luther looked back on those early years in the monastery, he viewed them mostly as one long nightmare—a single miserable block of time. As a result, it is impossible to form a timeline for the occurrence or duration of the various terrifying fears that occupied him. We don't know if he was continuously anxious and fearful, if his concerns waxed and waned, or if he was relatively free of symptoms for extended periods. From what he writes, it seems that he was tormented by fears on almost a daily basis.

Chapter *4*

DIAGNOSING OCD IN LUTHER'S EARLY MONASTERY YEARS

*O*ne of the main tasks in all medical specialties is to attach a label to a person's affliction so that other clinicians, as well as the patient, can understand something of its nature, course, and cause. Unfortunately, until fairly recently psychiatry failed miserably in this area. Even when I attended medical school in the 1970s, psychiatric diagnoses were mostly a matter of opinion. One psychiatrist would say a patient had one disorder, another would say she had another. Diagnoses often involved ambiguous psychoanalytic concepts. It's no wonder that clinicians of the past did not agree on Luther's diagnosis.

Finally, in 1980 a groundbreaking change occurred with the publication of a new and completely revamped, third edition of psychiatry's *Diagnostic and Statistical Manual*. Its stated purpose was to bring psychiatry into line with the rest of medicine by stressing reliability and validity in diagnosis. Reliability in this context means that different evaluators agree on the same diagnosis. Validity means that the diagnosis doesn't change over time. In order to accomplish this goal, the new manual presented exacting lists of clearly defined symptoms to distinguish each disorder. The most recent edition of the diagnostic manual, *DSM-V-TR*, published in 2022, continues to stress the same goals (Appendix B).

OCD has always been diagnosed on the basis of just two symptoms: obsessions and compulsions. In this sense, it is the simplest of all psychiatric disorders. Major depression, for example, requires the evaluation of nine symptoms, including depressed mood, diminished interests, weight loss, insomnia, and low energy. Panic disorder involves the assessment of more than a dozen complaints. But OCD involves only a particular form of thoughts—ideas, images, or urges—that are called obsessions, and the repeated acts that are made to deal with them, known as compulsions. If both symptoms are present, there is no doubt about the diagnosis. The symptoms, of course, must meet a certain standard of severity: They must be time consuming (e.g., take more than one hour per day) or cause clinically significant[1] distress or impairment in social, occupational, or other important areas of functioning.

Obsessions (sometimes called obsessional thoughts, or obsessional fears) are the primary symptom of OCD. They produce all the difficulties that lead people to seek treatment, including severe anxiety, time-consuming compulsions, and avoidance of important tasks. In our day, the term obsession has taken on a broad, which is to say vague, meaning. Most commonly, it is used to indicate a preoccupation, such as being "obsessed" with food or fashion. But the clinical meaning of the term, the one employed in this book, stays close to its Latin root, obsidere, meaning to besiege, as an army would surround and attack a city for the purpose of forcing surrender.

Obsessions are ideas, images, and urges that pop into the mind unbidden, cause terror, and cannot be dismissed. Although sometimes of a vile or repugnant nature, they are entirely normal thoughts for people to have. Obsessions differ from other thoughts only in how frequently and forcefully they pop into the mind, how strongly they are resisted, and how much fear they cause. They do not represent forms of delusions or hallucinations. They also are not related to addictions, which are fueled by the hope of short-term gratification. Obsessions are never pleasurable—they are always 100 percent unwanted.

Compulsions, OCD's other symptom, are purely secondary phenomena. An obsession strikes, and it must be addressed. Compulsive acts do the addressing. Popularly, the term compulsion is used to indicate anything done to excess. But again, the clinical meaning is much more specific. Put simply, compulsions are repeated, futile attempts to put right an obsessional fear. Typically, they are physical behaviors, observable acts performed to prevent something bad from happening. Well-recognized examples include washing and cleaning, checking, and requesting reassurance from others. Like the tormenting thoughts that fuel them, compulsions are never pleasurable. Sometimes they cause medical problems themselves.

In the latest edition of the diagnostic manual, obsessions and compulsions are identified by these criteria (somewhat tightened for clarity):

• Obsessions: Recurrent and persistent thoughts, urges, or images that are experienced, at some time during the disturbance, as intrusive and unwanted. They cause marked anxiety or distress.

- Compulsions: Repetitive behaviors (e.g., hand washing) or mental acts (e.g., praying) that the individual feels driven to perform in response to an obsession, and which are clearly excessive.

When considering the terrors suffered by Martin Luther, it is important to remember that unlike with many psychiatric disorders, the diagnosis of obsessive-compulsive disorder does not depend on observations about a patient's behavior (e.g., agitation, distractibility, erratic or inappropriate conduct). Nor does diagnosing OCD involve the administration of psychological tests. The diagnosis rests entirely on how a person describes his struggles. Since Luther describes his struggles plainly and lucidly, it is reasonable to think that a confidant diagnosis can be made, despite the dangers of doing so retrospectively.

It is entirely clear from Luther's own accounts that he suffered severely enough as a young man to warrant some sort of a psychiatric diagnosis. He referred to his terrible spiritual trials so often, and provided so much detail about them, that every one of his major biographers agrees that he endured a lengthy episode of major psychological turmoil. Descriptions of his mental state offered by his most respected and thorough biographers include "an acute sensitivity hardly reasonable," "the most frightful insecurities," "attacks of nameless, monstrous anxiety," and "severe attacks of a psychopathic nature."[2] Bainton sums up Luther during this period of his life as "a young man on the verge of a nervous collapse."[3]

LUTHER'S SYMPTOMS

In determining whether Martin Luther suffered from clinical obsessions, a good place to start is the autobiographical material he supplies in one his most famous and influential works,

Lectures on Galatians,[4] which he composed in his late forties. Galatians was Luther's favorite letter of the New Testament. He called it "my epistle, to which I am betrothed." Here are two relevant excerpts from the lectures:

> "When I was a monk, I used to think that my salvation was undone ... Therefore, I could not find peace, but I was constantly crucified by thoughts such as these: 'You have committed this or that sin; you are guilty of envy, impatience, etc.'"

> "My conscience could never achieve certainty but was always in doubt and said: 'You have not done this correctly. You were not contrite enough. You omitted this in your confession.' Therefore the longer I tried to heal my uncertain, weak, and troubled conscience with human traditions, the more uncertain, weak, and troubled I continually made it."

Luther tells us that he was "constantly crucified by thoughts," a marvelously informative description of what it is like to experience clinical obsessions. The more they are fought, the stronger they become. They seem irresistible, and demand to be addressed. As one patient told me, "I know it's an obsession when it seems like the most important thing in the world is for me to deal with it right now."

In other places, the Great Reformer writes:

> "My heart shivered and trembled as to how God could be merciful to me ... I was the most miserable creature on earth. Day and night there was nothing but horror and despair."[5]

"While conscience accuses, devils wheedle, and the wrath of God threatens, the wretched soul does nothing but tremble with horror at the judgment which may come at any time."[6]

"I was nursing incessant mistrust, doubt, fear, hatred, and blasphemy against God. I was superstitious to the point of delirium and insanity."[7]

To these quotes could be added many others. There is no doubt that Luther's crucifying thoughts (e.g., "you omitted this in your confession") meet the criteria given above for clinical obsessions. They were recurrent, persistent, intrusive, unwanted, and caused marked anxiety and distress.

There is one thing about Luther's obsessional fears that is somewhat unusual. Typically, OCD sufferers are able to realize that their obsessions are irrational or unrealistic—if not at the time they strike, then at least in a moment of quiet reflection soon afterward. Luther, however, did not believe that his fears were unrealistic, at least not until he began to overcome them. At times in psychiatry's past, a patient's insight into the irrational nature of his or her obsessions was considered essential for the diagnosis of OCD. Now, however, it is clear that insight is not always present. In particular, it often seems lacking in religious obsessions, most likely because these can be impossible to refute through logic. An obsessional fear of germs can be shown to be unreasonable by scientific studies. But what can assure an individual that she is not eternally damned? As one patient told me, "Well, Dr. Osborn, some Christians are not saved. How can I be sure I'm not one of them?"

Compulsions are the most readily identifiable symptom of OCD. Luther performed a large array of compulsions during his early monastery years. By and large, they involved works performed over and over in an effort to assuage his fear that he had not completed them correctly. Luther sums them up: "I could not but imagine that I had angered God, whom I in turn had to appease by doing good works."[8]

These compulsive works were primarily of three types: confessions, acts of self-abnegation, such as fasting and forgoing sleep, and prayers.

Confessions. In the Roman Catholic Church, confession of sins is an essential rite, one of seven officially recognized sacraments in which a person directly experiences the grace of God. In this holy moment, a believer confides his sins to a priest who, on behalf of God, absolves him of responsibility for these sins. Devout Catholics typically gain some degree of peaceful consolation from this humble act. Luther did not. He confessed the same sins repeatedly, yet his conscience still told him he had not done so correctly.

Repeated, excessive confessing is Luther's most obvious symptom of OCD. "Confession was a wretched torment,"[9] he writes. "After confession and the celebration of Mass, I was never able to find rest in my heart."[10] Most commonly, his compulsive confessing was fueled by concern that he had not shared all of his important sins. Luther writes that he "never seemed able to confess sufficiently certain sins, and incessantly and restlessly sought one absolution after the other, one father confessor after the other."[11] He further observes,

> "When I was young, I had to bare myself so completely to my pastor that he might know what I did every day of my life. So I told everything I had done from my youth up, with the result that my preceptor

in the monastery finally reprimanded me for doing so."[12]

Luther once mentioned that his favorite saint during his years in the monastery was Doubting Thomas, the disciple who stubbornly refused to believe in the reality of the Risen Christ. Sometimes, his problem in the confessional was doubting whether he had been absolved of the sins he had already confessed.

> "I could not accept the absolution which those to whom I confessed brought me. This was the way I thought: 'Who knows whether such consolations should be believed?' Later on, by chance I asked my preceptor, amid many tears, about these many temptations of mind which I was suffering. . . He said to me: 'Son, what are you doing?'"[13]

Luther's terrifying uncertainties led him to engage in extraordinarily long confessions. While the monks at Erfurt were required to confess once a week, Luther confessed daily, engaging his confessor for up to six hours at a time, splintering even the smallest sin into chains of minute details. When finally finished, he sometimes asked if he could start over again.[14] As a result, Luther writes, "No confessor wanted to have anything to do with me."[15] One told Luther, "You are a fool. God is not incensed against you, but you are incensed against God."[16] Another told him, "Look here, if you expect Christ to forgive you, come in with something to forgive—parricide, blasphemy, adultery—instead of these scruples!"[17] According to a fellow monk, Luther was threatened that if he didn't stop his inappropriate behaviors, he would be disciplined for obstruction of confession."[18]

Acts of self-abnegation. Since the early years of the Christian Church, these have been considered an essential part of monastic practice. The basic idea is that people can overcome unwanted desires, and therefore grow closer to God, by developing habits in the opposite direction. For instance, in order to extinguish an inordinate fondness of food and comfort, an individual can train himself to endure fasts and harsh conditions. This practice worked for other monks, but not for Luther. He gained nothing from severe vigils and fasts. In his *Lectures on Genesis*, written in 1541, he looks back with disgust on his attempts to please God through ascetic behaviors.

> "Formerly, when I was a monk, I was far saintlier than I am now so far as the external mask is concerned. I prayed more, kept vigils, practiced abstinence, and tormented my flesh. I was intensely crushed and distressed… By fasting, abstinence, and austerity in the matter of work and clothing I nearly killed myself. My body was horribly tormented and exhausted."[19]

Luther dug deeply into self-mortification, yet the result was a worsening of his physical and mental problems:

> "Only truly afflicted consciences fasted in earnest. I almost fasted myself to death, for again and again I went for three days without taking a drop of water or a morsel of food. I was very serious about it … If I had kept on any longer, I should have killed myself with vigils, prayers, reading and other work."[20]

Some great Catholic saints have pursued fasting and other acts of self-abnegation to the point of seriously endangering their health. Whether such behaviors are the result of OCD hinges on the question of whether they are driven primarily by fear. I have never treated a person with compulsive ascetical practices, but I have worked with men who are clinically compulsive bodybuilders. There is a similarity: While one seeks to become more holy and the other to become more attractive, both expend great effort to accomplish what appears to be a positive goal. In both, as well, the great majority of people engaged in these pursuits do not suffer from OCD. But if the bodybuilder's seemingly excessive behaviors are driven by an obsessional fear (e.g., "I look ugly") then OCD may be present. Similarly, if extreme ascetical practices are driven by dread of God's punishment, OCD may be involved.

The telltale sign of compulsive behaviors is that they don't achieve the desired goal. No matter how much muscle he gains, the clinically compulsive bodybuilder can never overcome the fear of not being muscular enough. Likewise, despite his great acts of mortification, Luther could never believe that he had satisfied God.

> "With all my Masses, with prayers, fasts, vigils, and chastity I never advanced to the point where I could say: 'Now I am certain that God is gracious to me.'... I wounded my conscience with those acts of righteousness, with the result that even now it can scarcely be restored."[21]

Prayers. When Luther attempted to pray, he often was overwhelmed by doubts. He writes,

"In ourselves we experience this crowd of thoughts upbraiding us: 'Why do you want to pray? Do you not know what you are and what God is?'... I have learned from my own experience that these thoughts often drove prayer away from me."[22]

In response to his doubts, he would be forced to repeat his prayers over and over again. Prayer becomes compulsive when it turns into a mere repetition of words, a meaningless, spiritually dry ritual. Luther suggests that this happened to him. He talks of "all those prayers I mumbled for fifteen whole years," and notes specifically that he "often repeated the words very coldly."[23] He "tortured" himself with prayers, and weakened himself to such an extent that he "would not have lasted much longer."[24] Excessively repeated prayers are common compulsions among devout individuals with OCD. The majority of Christians I work with engage in compulsive prayer. It seems likely that Luther did as well.

Luther's lengthy and repetitive confessions, and probably his prayers and labored acts of self-mortification as well, satisfy the criteria for compulsions. His all-consuming fear of God's wrath easily satisfies the diagnostic criteria for clinical obsession. Any person today who presented this history to a competent psychiatrist would receive a psychiatric diagnosis, and the diagnosis would be obsessive-compulsive disorder.

During his long ordeal, Luther appears to have survived by maintaining a somewhat precarious balance between dealing with his fears and performing his duties. All the while, he was actively looking for a solution to his problems. As noted by Brecht, "Luther's inmost identity was at stake [and] he devoted himself to a persistent search for a way out."[25] Luther was never able to find that way through the theology he was taught. Fortunately, however, as a result of his intensive bible study, the light would eventually break through on his obsessions and bring him peace.

Chapter 5

LUTHER'S CURE FOR HIS WORKS OBSESSIONS

*P*sychiatrists themselves were stumped for a long time in their attempts to find a cure for OCD. The great psychoanalyst Sigmund Freud, who wrote more papers on OCD than any other disorder, admitted that this one baffled him. His own theories on the subject, he once said, were no more than "doubtful assumptions and unconfirmed suppositions."[1] When I was in medical school, one clinician of that era wrote, "Most of us are agreed that the treatment of obsessional states is one of the most difficult tasks confronting the psychiatrist, and many of us consider it hopeless."[2]

Not until the 1980s did an effective psychological cure for OCD become widely employed. In essence, the treatment is simple. The gist of it is found in an old adage that most people have heard all their lives: Face up to your fears. The treatment is called exposure and response prevention therapy (ERP). Its effectiveness is due to an inborn, physiological property of the nervous system called habituation. If a snail's head is lightly touched, it recoils quickly into its shell. If it is touched fifteen times in a row, however, the head stops withdrawing. The snail, in effect, gets used to being touched. That's habituation. The same type of response occurs in the infinitely more complicated case of a person who is fearful of something. Like the snail, if she is presented repeatedly with a noxious stimulus (i.e., the object of her fear), and neither escapes from it nor is harmed by it, then she will eventually get used to it.

ERP was first used in the 1950s to treat simple phobias. Suppose an individual has an irrational fear of riding in elevators. In order to get over her fear, she must first make herself go into an elevator—she must expose herself to the anxiety-producing situation. Then she must prevent herself from running out of the elevator—this is called response prevention. Research suggests that if she steps into elevators a sufficient number of times (about thirty), and each time stays on the elevator long enough to allow her anxiety to diminish (as a rule, not longer than an hour), she will gradually habituate to her fear and overcome her phobia.

The application of ERP to clinical obsessions is much less straightforward than phobias, mainly because obsessions involve terrifying thoughts (like being damned) rather than real-life situations (such as being on an elevator). The more you try to get them out of your mind, the stronger these thoughts come back. According to prevailing theory for much of the twentieth century, obsessions were caused by deep-seated, pathological, unconscious conflicts. To directly expose a person to such conflicts, it was believed, could lead to a sudden unleashing of them, which could result in outright psychosis. Fortunately, the brilliant English psychologist Victor Campbell Meyer proved in the 1970s that obsessional fears can be effectively treated in the same way as phobias, by ERP (see Appendix C).

Therapists in the present day employ a number of different methods for exposing people to their obsessional thoughts. These include real-life exposures (e.g., a person with an obsessional fear of germs touches a toilet); imaginal exposures (e.g., a person with an obsessional fear of damnation conjures a vivid image of hell); and, most simply, encouraging a person to repeatedly bring a fearful, unwanted thought to mind, and keep it there front and center. Hundreds of published studies show that ERP therapy is able to markedly help 60 to 80 percent of OCD sufferers. By now a number of additional psychological treatments have been proven helpful for OCD,[3] but ERP remains the gold standard.[4] Among therapists who specialize in the disorder there is general agreement that ERP is essential in difficult cases.

Remarkably, Luther, in his pre-psychological age, found his way to the same conclusion. He was able to overcome his works obsessions as a result of striking insights he had into the meaning of scripture. We will see that, from a clinical point of view, these insights proved effective because they led him to employ a strong form of ERP therapy.

Lectures on Psalms (1513-1515)

Fortune began to turn for Martin Luther when in 1512 his superior in the monastery, Father Johannes von Staupitz,[5] made a momentous decision. Staupitz ordered Luther to leave Erfurt and assume the prestigious position of chief of bible studies at a newly formed Augustinian University in Wittenberg, a small town a hundred miles to the northeast. There, in addition to administrative tasks and his normal duties as a priest, Luther's job would be to teach and interpret scripture, starting with the book of Psalms.

It was risky for Staupitz to promote Luther to this new position. He, more than anyone else, knew of Luther's struggles. He had served not only as Luther's superior, but also as his confessor, spiritual director, and closest friend in the monastery. Biographer Roland Bainton captures the delicacy of the situation: "A young man on the verge of a nervous collapse over religious problems was to be commissioned as a teacher, preacher, and counselor to sick souls."[6]

Perhaps Staupitz took the gamble, at least in part, in the hope that Luther would find an answer to his tormenting doubts by intensively studying scripture and searching for its deepest meanings. Up to that point, no teacher in the monastery had been able to help him.

Arriving in Wittenberg at age twenty-nine, Luther quickly warmed to his first assignment. Psalms was a book of extraordinary importance to monks. More than any other part of the Bible, it provided them with the language and imagery for speaking about God. Luther himself called the Psalter "a little Bible [in which] is comprehended most beautifully and briefly everything that is in the entire Bible."[7] He prepared extensively for his classes. For his textbook, he chose a new translation of the Latin Vulgate Bible prepared by the man who would become his great theological adversary, Erasmus of Rotterdam. Already fluent in Latin, Luther learned Hebrew in order to compare Erasmus's version with original texts. He filled his lectures with quotes from a half dozen commentaries—Augustine alone is quoted 270 times. He composed detailed notes for each lecture and made copies for his students on the recently invented printing press. Luther would lecture on Psalms twice a week for two full years. Although the lectures themselves are not preserved, Luther's notes for about two-thirds of them remain available. Even a pared-down version of them fills two large volumes in the American edition of *Luther's Works*.

Luther's job was to dig deeply into each of the 150 Psalms, critically examining its verses and interpreting its meaning. He was permitted and even encouraged to show originality in his exegetical work, as long as he stayed within the general framework of Catholic teachings. In expounding the Psalms' meanings, Luther began with the traditional assumptions of the Christian Church fathers: The crucial principle was that everything in the Psalms pointed to Christ. In this regard, the terms "Lord" and "King" refer to Christ, and Christ himself speaks through David. Jerusalem is the "eternal Kingdom of Christ" and Israel's deliverance from captivity is the redemption of the whole world by Christ. Luther also did not hesitate to develop his own allegories. He later poked fun at himself for how much he read into certain verses: "I used to allegorize everything; I even allegorized the privy."[8]

In the end, Staupitz's gamble paid off. Luther proved a brilliant teacher; during his lectures on Psalms, he cured his tormenting fears about his works. This turnabout occurred just in time. Luther later said, "If it had not been for Dr Staupitz, I would have sunk into hell."[9]

DISCOVERIES IN PSALMS

As Luther pored over the text of the Psalter looking for its deepest meanings, he experienced a great awakening: David, the psalmist, suffered the same sort of agonizing spiritual trials as his own. As put by Luther's excellent biographer, Martin Brecht,

"Luther recognized that the psalms speak about those who undergo Anfechtungen, and therefore they are the ones who are especially capable of understanding and praying the psalms. Luther was able to treat his experiences theologically. In a unique fashion, the situation of the interpreter and the text he was interpreting came together."[10]

In the Penitential Psalms, in particular, Luther found his own condition spelled out. In Psalm 51, for instance, one of Luther's favorites, David prays fervently,

"Have mercy on me, O God,
according to Thy steadfast love.
For I know my transgressions,
and my sin is ever before me.
Against Thee, Thee only, have I sinned,
and done that which is evil in Thy sight."

This was Luther's situation exactly. Just as David has "done that which is evil" in God's sight, and his sins are "ever before" him, Luther believed he had failed God in his works, and the thought of God's punishment tormented him.

Yet David makes sense of his situation in a manner that Luther had not considered before, or at least not applied to himself.

"Behold, I was brought forth in iniquity, and in sin did my mother conceive me."

The psalmist realizes that he has been a sinner from the day of his birth, and that he will never stop being a sinner. Therefore, he fully deserves damnation. In his lecture notes to Psalm

51, Luther admonishes his students: "In case someone does not yet understand that no one is righteous before God, the following expresses it clearly: 'Behold, I was brought forth in iniquity.'"[11]

David realizes that he can do nothing himself to change his terrible situation. So he simply throws himself on God's mercy, and prays that God will change his heart.

> "Create a clean heart in me, O God ... purge me with Hyssop, and I shall be clean; wash me and I shall be whiter than snow."

David's approach is effective. As he writes in Psalm 32,

> "I acknowledged my sin to you,
> and I did not cover my iniquity;
> I said, 'I will confess my transgressions to the
> LORD,'
> and you forgave the iniquity of my sin."

For a half-dozen years, Luther had been desperately trying to deal with his fear of God's punishment by perfecting his works. Yet the psalmist proceeded much differently. Since a general rule of biblical exposition is that what applies to David applies to all of us, Luther was struck to the core by the biblical truth that we are all sinners who deserve damnation. Our only hope for salvation is to confess our failures and throw ourselves on God's mercy, even as we realize that we don't deserve his mercy at all.

David's humility became Luther's model for how to deal with a burden of sinfulness that cannot be overcome. Luther deduced that the strength of David's approach is that he told the truth. God values truth above all because Christ himself is truth. In his class notes, Luther observes,

> "He who judges himself and confesses his sin justifies God and affirms His truthfulness, because he is saying about himself what God is saying about him.... It is impossible for one who confesses his sin not to be righteous, for he speaks the truth. But where the truth is, there is Christ."[12]

In the Psalms, then, Luther uncovered an entirely new perspective on his obsessional fears. The good news was that God could be merciful to him even if he never succeeded in his works. Furthermore, there was no point in trying over and over to perfect his works since this was impossible. These were great insights. As a rule, however, more than just an intellectual insight is necessary to cure a bad case of OCD. What is needed is exposure and response prevention therapy. Amazingly, Luther found a way to accomplish this as well.

TO ACCUSE AND CONDEMN

Thus far Luther's renderings of the psalmist's words have been fairly straightforward, remaining within the scope of a branch of medieval theology called humility piety. Centuries before, Saint Bernard of Clairvaux had called for an attitude of constant repentance. Now, however, Luther begins to take some exegetical liberties. What is involved in truthfully confessing one's sins? For the psalmist, nothing more than "saying," "speaking," or "admitting" them to God. Luther, however, proceeds to interpret the psalmist in a more radical manner. Where David says in Psalm 32, "I will confess my transgressions to the Lord," Luther's paraphrase is striking:

"That is: 'I will rebuke myself; then God will praise
me. I will degrade myself; then God will honor me.
I will accuse myself; then God will acquit me. I will
speak against myself; then God will speak for me. I
will speak of my guilt; then He will speak about my
merit.'"[13]

Luther deduces that it is the person who magnifies his sins
the most who gives God the highest praise, because by magnifying them, he also magnifies the mercy that God shows in
forgiving him.

"It is not possible to make the mercy of God large and
good, unless a person first makes his miseries large
and evil. The more deeply a person has condemned
himself and magnified his sins, the more is he fit for
the mercy and grace of God."[14]

For an individual suffering terrifying thoughts of God's condemnation, Luther's words amount to a strong prescription for
exposure and response prevention therapy. Luther advocates
constantly, purposefully, and forcefully bringing into mind the
very thoughts that cause torment.

How might a modern-day OCD therapist employ ERP to
treat obsessional fears like Martin Luther's? As put succinctly
by one leading OCD researcher, "You have to purposefully
think your unwanted distressing thoughts in order to make
them less frightening."[15] Psychologist Joseph Ciarrocchi, in his
excellent book on the treatment of religious obsessions, pres-
ents an effective treatment for an obsession that Luther appears to have suffered, "God will punish me." The individual

should "intentionally provoke the obsession and dwell on the obsession for 15 to 90 minutes daily."[16]

It is clear that Luther accomplished what modern therapists prescribe. He says that we should condemn ourselves with specific accusations such as these: "I am a liar," "I am evil," "I am stupid," "I am blind," "I have fallen," "I am wretched," "I am nothing," "I am a sinner and have done evil," and "against Thee have I sinned."[17] How long might Luther have spent condemning himself? Most likely even longer than Ciarrocchi suggests, because Luther says, "Our total concern must be to magnify and aggravate our sins, and thus always accuse them more and more."[18] This is a strong form of psychological medicine.

A modern therapist would likely also try to employ "exposure in the imagination," an especially strong form of ERP therapy. This involves conjuring up detailed images of a given obsessional fear coming true. Luther appears to have also exposed himself to his obsessions in this manner. Brecht notes that "Luther's concepts of the judging Christ were not abstract, vague theological thoughts, but concrete and graphic images."[19] In the context of magnifying our sins, we find Luther advising, "Imagine yourself to be already altogether condemned with all demons."[20] For an individual terrified of losing salvation, that would represent a hard-core exercise.

In order for ERP to be effective, compulsions must be prevented. A modern therapist would insist that a patient with Luther's compulsions immediately stop his excessive confessing, prayers, and ascetical practices. Luther, of course, didn't know what compulsions were. He did, however, have extraordinary motivation to stop all such practices—performing them was offensive to God. They represented nothing more than vain attempts to escape God's judgment on himself.

Luther probably cured his terrifying works obsessions within a year or two after beginning his lectures on Psalms. Oxford's Alister McGrath suggests that by late 1514, Luther had arrived at the insight that God bases righteousness on humility rather than works.[21] Luther's attraction to this position, and especially the self-abasing form of it which he developed, has puzzled Luther's biographers. Martin Brecht writes, "The cause of Luther's stubborn orientation towards the attitude of humility remains obscure."[22] The clinical perspective suggests that the reason was its therapeutic usefulness.

The fact is that little in scripture supports the conclusion that "our total concern must be to magnify and aggravate our sins." Within a couple of years, Luther would abandon the idea that righteousness is achieved through actively accusing and condemning ourselves. Furthermore, accusing and condemning himself, although a fine cure for his works obsessions, was not the final solution for his OCD. It left Luther vulnerable to other tormenting fears, and he soon would be struck by a new—and worse—obsession.

Yet as we shall see in the next chapter, the Great Reformer drew an enormously important conclusion from this episode.

Chapter **6**

WHAT LUTHER LEARNED
ABOUT WORKS

*T*he question of how a person gains right-standing before God was fiercely debated by the early Church fathers. In light of scripture, they concluded that righteousness is a cooperative venture between man and God. People play their part by trying to follow God's commands and accomplish good works, which might include penances, prayers, or charitable acts. For more than a thousand years, the Catholic Church maintained this position. Prior to Martin Luther, it was not a subject of controversy.

After curing his works obsessions, however, Luther proposed something radically different: Works play no role at all in a person's right-standing before God. God declares a person righteous (or "justifies"[1] the individual) all on his own. Luther makes this clear in his Lectures on Romans of 1515 to 1516:

> "The righteousness of God is brought to us without our merits and our works."[2]

Critically, Luther never in his life denied the importance of good works. The view he came to, however, is that a person performs works naturally after receiving God's gift of righteousness, out of both thankfulness to God and the activity of the Holy Spirit.

Luther's idea that works play no part in righteousness was revolutionary. How did he come to it? He said on a number of occasions that his spiritual trials (anfechtungen) were a help to him.

> "I didn't learn my theology all at once. I had to ponder over it ever more deeply, and my spiritual trials were of help to me in this, for one does not learn anything without practice."[3]

> "Only spiritual trial teaches what Christ is."[4]

> "If I live longer, I would like to write a book about Anfechtung, for without it no man can understand scripture, faith, the fear or the love of God."[5]

Luther's biographers readily acknowledge that his spiritual trials helped him to develop his theology. The experts, however, assume that Luther's fears simply served the role of a catalyst, prodding him to uncovering the truth in scripture. They suggest the following sequence of events. First, Luther's spiritual trials spurred him to bible study. This led him to find the real truth about works. Finally, his new understanding cured his fears.

Our clinical understanding of Luther's spiritual trials, however, suggests a different sequence of events. First, Luther's trials spurred him to bible study. This led him to find a cure for his fears (accusing and condemning himself). Finally, as a result of curing his fears, Luther came to a new understanding of the role of works in righteousness. It was from experiencing and curing his fears that Luther learned the truth. This is in fact the way the Great Reformer describes his experience. "Without [anfechtung] no man can understand scripture, faith, the fear or the love of God ... Only spiritual trial teaches what Christ is."

How does a person learn from an obsessional fear? The progression is a natural one. Consider the simple example of an individual with contamination obsessions and hand-washing compulsions. She sees a therapist who employs strong ERP, encouraging her to purposefully expose herself to contamination for lengthy periods of time every day, while refraining from washing her hands. Gradually she habituates to her fears and stops worrying that her hands are dangerously contaminated. She is finally able to draw a life-changing conclusion: Normal handwashing is sufficient for her cleanliness.

Similarly, Luther purposefully exposed himself to his tormenting works obsessions. He habituated to them and stopped worrying that he was unrighteous. Then he drew a life-changing conclusion: Works do not make a person righteous.

Although it makes perfect sense that Luther reevaluated the truthfulness of his fears after curing them, one might still wonder why Luther concluded that works play no part in attaining righteousness. Why didn't he decide that "normal" works are all that's necessary, just as the handwasher concludes that normal washing is sufficient? Had Luther decided that normal works were what is necessary for righteousness, the entire course of Western history might have been different.

One reasonable answer is that the Catholic Church's scandalous abuse of the doctrine of works influenced Luther to conclude that the whole thing should be scrapped. Given that he found scriptural support for a new position, this is what he chose to do. But there is another reason to consider from the clinical point of view. It involves the particular teaching that Luther received in his monastery about how a person becomes righteous. This was a fairly new approach that was not accepted in all monasteries.

At Erfurt, Luther was taught that in order to be declared righteous by God a person must "do what is in him" to follow God's commands, no more and no less.[6] According to this view, it is not important how successful an individual is in accomplishing good works. The important thing is that he gives his best effort. This teaching does not seem unreasonable; many Christians believe something similar today. It might even seem especially helpful for assuaging the consciences of believers worried about accomplishing their works.

Unfortunately, making righteousness depend on doing your best can wreak havoc for people prone to OCD, the doubting disease. Consider the individual with hand-washing compulsions. Suppose a friend gives her the advice, "Just do your best to get your hands clean." This sounds reasonable, yet might be the worst advice possible. It sets off in the mind of the doubter a terrible question: "How can I know if I'm doing my best?"

So it was with Luther. He could never rest comfortably in the knowledge that he was doing "what was in him" to accomplish the works that God asked him to do. He would later ruthlessly point out the flaw in this approach to righteousness.

> "If you say: Man should strive to do that which is in
> him, I would counter with the question whether he
> knows that he is striving and how he strives and what

he must do in order to strive? . . . Why teach that a
man should do what he does not know?"[7]

Interestingly, a few Catholic scholars have argued that if
Luther had learned the classic approach to righteousness in the
monastery, he would not have suffered severe spiritual trials.
This differed significantly from "do what is in you." It emphasized that while God does require a person to do identifiable
works in order to be declared righteous, these works can be best
accomplished through the slow process of acquiring virtuous
habits. Returning again to the handwasher, suppose her friend
told her to set specific goals in handwashing, such as incremen-
tally shortening the time she spends at it. It is hard to argue
that such an approach would not turn out much better than
simply saying "do your best."

In any case, Luther's idea that works play no part in righteousness was arguably the most important of all his great theological breakthroughs. It is this idea, more than any other, that
separates Protestants from Catholics. The followers of Rome
believe that God takes a person's good deeds into account, at
least to some degree, when he declares a person righteous before him, while the followers of Luther do not.

THE 95 THESES AND THE START
OF THE REFORMATION

It was Luther's new understanding of the role of works in
righteousness that led him to take a strong stand against his
church's use of the doctrine called "indulgences." On October
31, 1517, Luther posted ninety-five theses to the door of his
church in Wittenberg. They were entitled "Disputation on the
Power and Efficacy of Indulgences." From Luther's day to the

present, this date has been considered the birthday of the Reformation.

Indulgences were spiritual favors granted by the Pope as rewards for meritorious acts of charity and self-sacrifice. Their use was an old and established practice. Crusaders, for instance, had been granted the highest form of indulgence: the complete remission of all temporal punishment due for any sins confessed. Understandably, then, indulgences were sought by large numbers of Christians in Luther's day. He once earned them for himself and his family through one of the popular rites afforded to pilgrims, climbing the Holy Stairs in Rome that reputedly once stood in Jerusalem and had been climbed by Jesus.

During Luther's lifetime, the Church dramatically increased the power of indulgences: They could reduce the time that believers and their dead relatives would have to spend in purgatory. Previously, on a doctrinal level at least, the effect of indulgences pertained only to reducing the penalties that people had to suffer in this life for their sins. Then, when controversial Pope Leo X came to office in 1513 (one Catholic historian called his reign "one of the most severe trials to which God ever afflicted his church"),[8] the newly formulated doctrine of indulgences began to be scandalously abused as a way to make money.

Pope Leo's stated goal was to fund the building of Saint Peter's Cathedral in Rome. But it came to the point where tickets to heaven were being openly sold in the streets of Saxony. One particularly obnoxious monk named Johann Tetzel, as the story goes, strolled through the villages singing, "When the coin in the coffer rings, the soul from purgatory springs."

More than a few Catholic leaders spoke out against this embarrassing spectacle, recognizing it as a gross distortion of the Church's own teachings. But Martin Luther spoke out the strongest. In his ninety-five theses, Luther came down hard on the practice of indulgences. In thesis 32, for instance, he wrote,

> "Those who believe that they can be certain of their salvation because they have indulgence letters will be eternally damned, together with their teachers."[9]

Why did Luther argue so strongly? He was not by nature a rebel. When he posted his 95 theses, he never meant to incite a full-scale break with his Church. Even as he argued strongly against indulgences, he was polite to the point of bending over backward to the Pope. It is only an understanding of Luther's furious battle with his fears that makes clear his motivations. Martin Brecht sums up in an exceptionally clear way the personal reason Luther had for his aggressive stance in the indulgence controversy:

> "Luther's entire involvement in this matter [of indulgences], in which he then risked himself more and more, can certainly be understood only if one is aware of how intensely he felt himself personally affected by his own struggle. It was here that he strove in deep conscientiousness for solutions, and he sought and found them in the humble acceptance of himself as a sinner. [But] here he encountered a practice of the church through which it was claimed that one could buy oneself out of this sole possible mode of existence, a practice which appeared to permit a person to bargain with God and dispense with sincerity, a practice

that cheapened grace. That so contradicted his hard experiences and the insights he had gained with such difficulties that he could not be silent."[10]

Luther had little reason to think his ninety-five theses would make a great difference. Higher-ups in the Vatican did not pay much attention to criticism unless their authority was directly questioned. It so happened, however, that Luther's post caught the tail wind of a perfect storm brewing in his homeland. Germany remained at the time a collection of inefficiently governed city-states, essentially unchanged from medieval times. These principalities were no longer able to compete economically with the large, unified nations around them, and the common folk were suffering. Resentment was growing toward indulgence preachers asking for money. Luther observes in his ninety-five theses how some of his parishioners had begun to ridicule the Pope: "Why doesn't he, who is very rich, spend his own money building St Peter's?"[11]

Commoners were not the only ones feeling the pinch. Governors of the German fiefdoms were obliged to pay expensive taxes for being a part of the Holy Roman Empire, an ancient alliance between the European principalities and the Church. In theory, being a part of the Empire afforded the city-states protection and stability. But the exorbitant levies outweighed their value. The result was a growing spirit of rebellion against Rome among both peasants and princes.

After posting his theses in 1517, Luther became the visible face of this unrest and a kind of rock star in his homeland. People flocked to hear him speak, and the newly invented printing press churned out his writings. More and more anger was vented toward the Catholic Church, and the wheels began to turn that would lead to a full-scale revolution against Rome.

Chapter 7

OCD STRIKES AGAIN: THE
TERRORS OF PREDESTINATION

*A*t the start of the year 1515, Martin Luther was likely in high spirits. Not only had he cured his works obsessions, his lectures on Psalms had been a great success and he was gaining recognition as a first-rate theologian. Soon, his first book would be published, a reworking of his notes on the Penitential Psalms that would eventually be reprinted seven times due to popular demand. One might have thought that at this point in his life the thirty-one-year-old future reformer had nothing but smooth sailing ahead.

An interesting event occurred that summer, however, suggesting that Luther's anxiety problems were not completely solved. Concerns about his salvation returned acutely, and this time they were not related specifically to his works. Luther was walking in his priestly robes in a procession celebrating the Feast of Corpus Christi. In front of him was his superior, Father Staupitz, carrying a large monstrance exhibiting the Eucharist, the bread that Catholics believe has been changed into the body of Christ. Luther recalls at that moment becoming "terrified by the sacrament which Dr. Staupitz carried."[1]

It was again the terror of the judging Christ—the same fear that had struck Luther dumb when he offered his first Mass. That incident had been a harbinger for the onset of his terrifying works obsessions. This latest event portended the onset of a new siege of tormenting obsessional fears that would strike Luther with even greater fury. They centered on the idea that God had completely abandoned him. In the past, whatever his torments, Luther had never actually doubted the presence of God in his life. This was a new and devastating concern.

AM I PREDESTINED FOR SALVATION?

In spring of 1515, Luther started lecturing on Saint Paul's Letter to Romans. It is the longest of Paul's letters, and many believe it is the clearest and most comprehensive presentation of Christian theology to be found anywhere in the Bible. Luther once called it, "A bright light almost sufficient to illuminate the entire holy Scriptures."[2] It gave him many ideas to feast on.

One of the subjects discussed in Romans is the predestination of the elect to eternal life. Paul writes in Chapter 8, "Those whom God foreknew He also predestined to be conformed to the image of his Son." Saint Augustine, among others, interpreted this to mean that God has chosen before the beginning of time all the people who will receive eternal life. As Luther reflected carefully on this passage, a new and terrifying question began to nag at him: What if I am not one of the predestined? As noted by Brecht,

"Luther was not concerned with the issue of predestination prior to the Romans lectures, [but it became]
the most extreme inner peril he ever experienced."³

In his *Explanations of the 95 Theses*, published in 1518, Luther provides a hair-raising account of devastating fears about
predestination that occurred, apparently fairly recently, to a
man he "knew." It is widely agreed that Luther was referring
to himself. After observing that the worst pains of the condemned in purgatory are "terror, dread, trembling, fear, and
quaking," Luther explains that some people suffer the same
kinds of punishment in this life. It happens when God is "cut
off" from their sight.

"I myself 'knew a man' who claimed that he had often
suffered these punishments, in fact over a very brief
period of time. Yet they were so great and so much like
hell that no tongue could adequately express them, no
pen could describe them, and one who had not himself experienced them could not believe them. And
so great were they that, if they had been sustained or
had lasted for half an hour, even for one tenth of an
hour, he would have perished completely and all of
his bones would have been reduced to ashes. At such
a time God seems terribly angry, and with him the
whole creation. At such a time there is no flight, no
comfort, within or without, but all things accuse. At
such a time as that the psalmist mourns, 'I am cut off
from thy sight.' In this moment (strange to say) the
soul cannot believe that it can ever be redeemed."⁴

In *The Bondage of the Will*, written in 1525, Luther makes clear the frustration and torment that the thought of God's abandonment had caused him.

> "It gives the greatest possible offense to common sense or natural reason that God by his own sheer will should abandon, harden, and damn men as if he enjoyed the sins and the vast, eternal torments of his wretched creatures.... And who would not be offended? I myself was offended more than once, and brought to the very depth and abyss of despair, so that I wished I had never been created a man."[5]

Later in his life, Luther shared with others the fact that he had once suffered greatly over the issue of predestination. To an acquaintance who was "sorely troubled" about her eternal destiny, he wrote: "I know all about this affliction. I was myself brought to the brink of eternal death by it." To a woman who came to him complaining, "I do not know if I am predestined or not," Luther replied, "the devil was similarly vexing me."[6]

In *Lectures on Genesis*, Luther observes that Satan attacks people with the goal of instilling doubt in their minds.

> "Satan besets people today in strange ways in order to make them doubtful and uncertain, and eventually even to alienate them from the Word. 'For why should you hear the Gospel, since everything depends on predestination?' In this way he robs us of the predestination guaranteed through the Son of God and the sacraments. And if he attacks timid consciences with this trial, they die in despair, as would almost have happened to me."[7]

OCD besets people, we may note, in similar strange ways. Like Satan himself, obsessions are contrary to a person's nature, or egodystonic. Like Satan's arrows, the obsessions of the doubting disease seem to come from outside a person's self and barge their way in. And the attacks of both Satan and OCD strike hardest the people who are timid and anxiety prone.

It is reasonable to conclude that Luther's tormenting thoughts about predestination represented clinical obsessions. The accusations telling him that he would not be redeemed, "so great and so much like hell that no tongue could adequately express them," meet the essential criteria: They were recurrent and persistent ideas that he experienced as intrusive and unwanted, and they cause marked anxiety and distress.

MENTAL COMPULSIONS

Whether Luther's struggles with predestination can be diagnosed as a full-fledged case of obsessive-compulsive disorder boils down to whether he developed clinical compulsions. Proving that he did is more difficult than it was in his first episode. To review, psychiatry's most recent *Diagnostic and Statistical Manual* defines compulsions as:

> (1) Repetitive behaviors (e.g., hand washing) or mental acts (e.g., praying) that the individual feels driven to perform in response to an obsession or according to rules that must be applied rigidly. [and] (2) The behaviors or mental acts are aimed at preventing or reducing anxiety or distress, or preventing some dreaded event or situation; however, these behaviors or mental acts are not connected in a realistic way

with what they are designed to neutralize or prevent, or are clearly excessive.

In Luther's lengthy first episode of OCD, his repetitive behaviors, such as excessive confessing, could easily be identified as clinical compulsions. In this case, however, Luther's compulsions appear to have been limited mainly to the mental acts mentioned in the definition above. These rituals are more difficult to recognize than repeated physical acts, not only for a clinician but also for the individual engaged in them. Although the example given in the *Diagnostic and Statistical Manual* is silent praying, in my experience mental compulsions most commonly involve endlessly examining and disputing an obsession in order to prove that is is groundless.

I once treated a devoutly religious student, for example, who would become terrified that she might have sinned while out on a date. She would have to carefully examine every aspect of her behavior: how she had dressed, how she stood, whether she touched her companion inappropriately at any time, whether she might have lusted, and on and on with a long list of possible transgressions. Compulsions of this sort could take up her whole day. Similarly, I treated a lawyer with terrifying fears that she angered God. She spent hours disputing with her fears in attempts to reassure herself of her innocence. "I try to prove that I'm not guilty of offending God," she said. "I imagine a court scene and conduct a trial. The prosecution argues the case that I am guilty, and I present the evidence for my innocence. As I talk, the jurors carefully weigh their decisions. It goes on and on with no resolution."

The evidence that Luther suffered from clinical compulsions in this second episode comes from his later writings. One example is found in a letter written in 1528, in which the Great Reformer addresses the problems of people who are "disturbed about thoughts of God and eternal salvation." Such thoughts, Luther explains, come from Satan, who tricks us into taking them seriously and trying to overcome them through reason.

> "He suggests such thoughts and makes them seem so important to us that we are unwilling to leave them or turn aside from them but wish to scrutinize them and think them through to the end."[8]

This is a textbook description of how OCD sufferers use mental compulsions: They scrutinize their obsessional thoughts and "think them through to the end." He also describes very clearly the characteristic sense of urgency those with OCD feel to address obsessional fears: They are "unwilling to leave or turn aside from them."

On other occasions, as well, Luther speaks about the torturous difficulties that arise when people question their status before God.

> "He [Luther] spoke of predestination and said that when a man begins to dispute about it, it is like a fire that cannot be extinguished, and the more he disputes the more he despairs."[9]

Elsewhere, Luther strongly warns people away from even thinking about whether they are predestined for heaven.

> "One is not free to have such thoughts or doubts about predestination; they are ungodly, vicious, and devilish."[10]

"It is ruinous and destructive, to think about the why."[11]

"God will not let Himself be taken captive and forced within the limits of your wisdom. His foreknowledge and predestination are no concern whatever of yours .... To think about the subject of predestination is either too difficult or too harsh for our feeble intellect to be able to grasp."[12]

These examples strongly suggest that Luther developed mental compulsions (i.e., mental acts aimed at preventing some dreaded event that are clearly excessive). This conclusion becomes almost certain, in my opinion, when another factor is considered. From a clinical perspective, it would be surprising if Luther had not developed a second episode of OCD. It is a general rule that when one strong obsession is beaten back through ERP, another obsession will always try to take its place. And unless a person again has a way to apply ERP, full-blown OCD will again develop. Furthermore, if a person continues to suffer tormenting obsessional fears over an extended period of time, she must almost necessarily be engaging in some sort of compulsions. If not, the natural process of habituation would have taken away the sting of the fears.

We will see that Luther did develop an effective therapeutic approach to his fears about predestination. He developed, in fact, a bible-based strategy that is applicable to all the fearful concerns that psychiatrists now refer to as clinical obsessions.

Chapter 8

LUTHER'S FINAL CURE: STAND ALONE AND ENDURE THE HAND OF GOD

*T*o cure his works obsessions, Luther had learned from the psalmist a new approach to gaining God's favor: Rather than attempting to perfect his works, he agreed with God's harsh judgment on himself, and appealed to God's mercy. Yet his agonizing concerns about predestination now seemed insoluble. If God had abandoned him, then God would never even hear his appeal. There was nothing he could do to win God back. Luther puts his finger on the exact nature of the dilemma:

> "It is difficult enough for a wretched conscience to believe. How can one believe at all if, to begin with, doubt is cast upon the object of one's belief? Thereby doubt and despair are only strengthened and confirmed."[1]

From a clinical perspective, one would think that in order to overcome these new obsessional fears, Luther must have found a new way to employ ERP therapy. This he did. But while his first approach had been highly active ("accuse and condemn yourself"), this time his approach was completely passive. It involved only enduring the hand of God painfully at work in him.

Luther's cure of his predestination obsessions began when he studied the writings of certain Catholic theologians of the fourteenth century who believed that people can attain union with God through willingly bearing their suffering. In particular, Luther was impressed with the writings of the Dominican priest Johannes Tauler (1300–1361). Tauler is appreciated as one of the great mystics of the Roman Catholic Church, and was popular among both monastics and educated lay people in Germany during Luther's time.

"WELCOME BITTER AFFLICTION"...
THE SERMONS OF TAULER

In 1516, Luther is known to have been studying Tauler's sermons. He soon became captivated by Tauler's descriptions of the "strange abandonment by God that leaves the spirit tortured." Here, for the first time, Luther found someone who understood his own affliction. Tauler gives an account of it that could have been written by Luther himself.

> "The man is now left so completely on his own that he knows nothing at all of God; he is brought to such desolation that he wonders whether he was ever on the right path, whether he has a God or not, whether he really exists; he is so strangely afflicted, so deeply afflicted, that he feels that the whole wide world has become too narrow for him. He can neither taste God

nor know him, and since everything else is insufficient, he feels himself hemmed in between two walls with a sword behind him and a sharp spear in front."

Not only did Tauler know what it was like to suffer such a trial, he offered a solution for it. Tauler continues:

"What is he to do? Let him sit down and say: 'Welcome bitter affliction, full of grace' [For] when our Lord has prepared a man's soul by such intolerable trials, [he] then comes and raises the soul to the highest stage. And here Our Lord gives him new eyes to see and reveals to him the truth."[2]

It is through bearing our suffering and dying to self, Tauler says, that God draws us to him.

"We try to avoid taking up the cross, and that way we commit to a grave injustice. One should assume that burden freely, lift it right up to God, and then accept it as one's very own, be the circumstances external or internal, corporal or spiritual. Thus one is drawn into God."[3]

Tauler believed that being drawn into God in this manner led a person to a transcendent state where "the spirit rests [in] the secret silence of the divine Essence."[4] Luther would find that union with God led to a different grace: faith in God's promises. Yet on the basis of what he learned from Tauler, Luther was able to cure his terrifying fears of God's abandonment. Luther wrote to a friend in 1516, "Get for yourself the sermons of John Tauler... I have seen no theological work in Latin or

German that is more sound and more in harmony with the gospel than this."[5]

LUTHER'S THERAPY FOR PREDESTINATION FEARS

Luther's predestination fears, having begun in 1515 or 1516 as he started his lectures on St Paul's Letter to the Romans, were gone in 1518. At that time we find the Great Reformer writing in detail about these sorts of terrors, yet now with the assurance of one who had experienced them and knew how to overcome them.

More than in any other place, Luther writes about the terrors of God's abandonment in *Commentary on the First Twenty-Two Psalms* (*Operationes in Psalmos*), a multivolume work composed over the years 1518 to 1520. Here Luther provides straightforward advice for dealing with fears about predestination and God's abandonment. Much of it turns on the idea that Jesus himself suffered the terror of God's abandonment when he took our sins upon himself on the cross. We can join Jesus in his suffering, a spiritual martyrdom of sorts, when we willingly bear our own crosses of fear and doubt.

At the start of Psalm 22 David cries out, "My God, my God, why have you abandoned me." Luther begins his commentary on this Psalm by reminding his readers, "Let no one doubt that the first verse of this Psalm is to be understood wholly of Christ: for he himself used it as a prayer upon the cross." Luther says that Jesus' situation on the cross "frightened him so horribly that he experienced greater anguish than any man has ever experienced."[6] This is the same horrible fright, Luther explains, that occurs when "the soul is brought to that highest of all perils, predestination."[7]

What then is the person to do? "Christ is wholly silent," Luther observes, "for an example unto us that we should do the same." Luther counsels,

> "Before all things, let [the soul] take heed that it dispute not with devils and evil cogitations concerning all these things, let it give no answer, but remain dumb to all these things. [Although] it is a hard thing to keep silence and to remain wholly quiet, and permit all these most irritating and most bitter suggestions and sayings to pass by, but still, as there is no other way in which it can be accomplished, we must labour hard to do it."[8]

Luther says we are to follow the example of Jesus, to "remain dumb," and to "permit" the bitter suggestion that God has abandoned us. In clinical terms, this amounts to willingly exposing ourselves to the terrifying fear. Luther also provides clear instructions for preventing what we call mental compulsions. The individual should "take heed that it dispute not with devils and evil cogitations concerning all these things." Luther's clinical acumen is remarkable. This is straightforward advice to stop mental compulsions.

Psalm 6 involves David's fears of God's rebuke. In *Commentary on the First Twenty-Two Psalms*, Luther explains that this fear entails "a dread and horror of conscience before the face of the judgement of God." It is the same terror that Christ experienced in his passion. Addressing the question of what a person should do in a similar situation when "the conscience feels nothing else than that eternal damnation is its portion."[9] Luther observes,

> "This Psalm teaches us that if any one be pressed in these straits, he should flee unto no other than the angry God himself... [He should] not wander away, not complain, and not seek the consolations of men; but stand alone and endure the hand of God."[10]

The individual is to "stand alone and endure." This is the essential strategy for inducing habituation to any noxious stimulus: Allow it and don't respond to it. In his *First Lectures on Psalms*, Luther's advice to people suffering fears of God's rebuke had been to "accuse and condemn yourself." Here, Luther's advice is entirely different. It is to endure the hand of God, a completely passive approach.

In his discussion of Psalm 5 in *Commentary on the First Twenty-Two Psalms*, Luther sums up in striking manner his theological understanding of what happens when a person willingly endures the anfechtung of God's abandonment.

> "I will, therefore, in my mad way (as they say of me) show how I understand these matters. [T]he sinner is not justified, unless he be first condemned; he is not made alive, unless he be first killed; he ascendeth not into heaven, unless he first descend into hell; as the whole scripture plainly shows. Wherefore, the infusion of grace must of necessity be attended with bitterness, tribulation, and suffering; under which the old man groans, not being able to bear his casting out with any kind of patience. But if under this tribulation the man be patient, and wait for the hand of him that is working in him, [he] is thereby proved, and he shall find hope, faith, and love, which, under such an experience are infused."[11]

Luther's description of how God provides grace corresponds closely to how the process of habituation provides relief. Luther says, "the infusion of grace must of necessity be attended with bitterness, tribulation and suffering." That's the way it is with inducing habituation through exposure and response prevention—it occurs only if an individual strongly experiences the emotion of fear. Luther writes that in order to find grace a person must "wait for the hand of him that is working in him." Likewise, in ERP therapy, a person must have patience and wait for results; it takes a while for habituation to replace fear.

Lastly, in considering how Luther overcame his predestination obsessions, it is helpful to consider a sermon that he delivered, most likely in 1521. It is entitled "Tröstung für eine Person in hohen Anfechtungen," usually translated as, "Comfort When Facing Grave Temptations."[12] Luther's topic is David's terrifying situation in Psalm 142 when he is trapped by people trying to kill him. In Luther's exegesis, David is trapped by tormenting thoughts of loss of salvation. In this sermon, Luther takes from the Psalm five steps for dealing with such terrors. They correspond to a therapist's helpful suggestions.

1. "First, such a person must by no means rely on himself, nor must he be guided by his own feelings." ERP therapists routinely suggest to their patients that they not rely on themselves to decrease their anxiety, but rather on the process of habituation.

2. "Second, he must not imagine that he is the only one assailed about his salvation." Therapists always assure their patients that they are not alone; OCD is a common anxiety disorder.

3. "Third, he should by no means insist on deliverance from these trials without yielding to the divine will. He

should address God cheerfully and firmly and say, "If I am to drink this cup, dear Father, may your will, not mine, be done." This, from a clinical standpoint, is direct advice to expose oneself to obsessional fears.

4. "Fourth, there is no stronger medicine for this than to begin with words such as David used when he said in Psalm 18 [:3], 'I will call upon the Lord and praise him, and so shall I be saved from all that assails me.'" Here, Luther is installing hope and courage for the difficult assignment that lies ahead of willingly suffering the cross of fear and doubt. Encouraging hope is a critical step in ERP therapy.

5. "Fifth," Luther explains, "he must thank God diligently for deeming him worthy of such a visitation, of which many thousands of people remain deprived." Again, it is possible to find a clinical correlation if "visitation" involves gaining an understanding of how to deal with tormenting thoughts of loss of salvation. Many thousands of OCD sufferers are deprived of a good treatment strategy, and as a rule OCD sufferers are extremely grateful when they get it. One of my patients told me, "I divide my life into two stages: before I learned how to treat obsessive-compulsive disorder, and ever since then."

APPRAISING LUTHER'S CURES

Luther's cure for predestination obsessions is strong ERP therapy. He continually emphasizes exposure to fears ("endure the hand of God," "permit God to work," "remain dumb," "keep silent"). He even encourages people to let themselves be overwhelmed by their fears, which amounts to the therapeutic strategy called flooding ("become dead and buried"). Luther also gives specific instructions to refrain from what we call mental compulsions ("dispute not with devils and evil cogitations concerning all these things"). All of this amounts to a powerful program.

Yet, it is also true that a modern therapist might find Luther's approach falling short in one way. The most effective ERP exercises usually involve purposefully evoking obsessional fears and staying in their presence. Luther, however, does not recommend this. In his first cure, as we have seen, he recommended purposefully evoking fears ("accuse and condemn yourself," "imagine yourself to be already altogether condemned with all demons"). But the approach Luther took from Tauler involves simply being passive.

There are two factors, however, that make Luther's cure for his predestination obsessions an especially strong one. First, since Luther was being struck constantly by these obsessions, there was probably little need to purposefully evoke them. Second, Luther had an extraordinarily strong motive for pursuing his therapeutic strategy: It led to an actual union with God.

Chapter **9**

JUSTIFICATION BY GRACE
THROUGH FAITH

*A*fter overcoming his predestination obsessions, most likely some time in 1517, Luther deduced two momentous conclusions regarding how a person becomes righteous. First, he concluded that a person is justified (declared righteous) by God's grace alone. The individual plays no part in it—no purposeful acts, including accusing oneself, are involved in any way. Second, Luther reasoned that justification comes through believing—that is, through faith.

Luther's biographers generally attribute his discoveries about grace and faith to further breakthroughs in his understanding of scripture as he continued his lectures on the New Testament during the years 1516 to 1518. The clinical model, however, again provides additional insight. It suggests that Luther's conclusions about grace and faith were logical given what he learned from curing his obsessional fears.

We have seen that Luther overcame his tormenting doubts about his righteousness only after he gave up hope in his own ability to overcome them. What then cured his doubts? Luther would never have considered any psychological explanation. Given the entirely God-centered Christian worldview of his time, it was entirely reasonable for Luther to conclude that God cured them. And when were his doubts cured? Obviously, when he started to believe what before he had questioned. They were cured when he became certain he was righteous. They were cured through having faith! Luther's conclusion is straightforward: We are justified by God's grace (declared righteous by God) through faith (when we believe we are righteous).

Luther most clearly states his new understanding of the role of grace and faith in the process of becoming righteous in one of his most important theological works, the Heidelberg Disputation of 1518.[1] This relatively short—yet theologically rich—presentation, delivered to an influential group of Augustinian theologians, is considered to be the most concise and carefully worded of all Luther's writings.

The Disputation consists of twenty-eight forceful statements. All of them deal with the same topic, the very matter that had haunted Luther much of his life: How does a person become righteous before God?

Luther begins his discussion by emphasizing a point that could be taken from a modern therapy manual for compulsive Christians.

> "Human works which are done over and over again cannot advance man on his way to righteousness."

Luther then makes short work of the theology of justification he learned in the monastery.

"The person who believes that he can obtain grace by doing what is in him adds sin to sin."

After this, Luther turns his attention to the truths he had learned from overcoming his predestination fears. First of all, it is only through complete passivity in the face of terrifying fears of God's abandonment that a person can find righteousness.

"It is certain that man must utterly despair of his own ability before he is prepared to receive the grace of Christ."

Luther then introduces one of his richest theological constructs, referred to as his "Theology of the Cross." It says that we must join Jesus on his cross of fear and despair in order to find God.

"True theology and recognition of God are in the crucified Christ.... God can be found only in suffering and the cross."

It is important to note that although Luther later applies his theology of the cross to all types of suffering—physical and mental—in the Heidelberg Disputation he is talking specifically about suffering the fear of imminent death.

"To be born anew, one must consequently first die and then be raised up with the Son of Man. To die, I say, means to feel death at hand."

Gerhard Forde, in his excellent book on the Heidelberg Disputation, clarifies what Luther means by the words "to feel death at hand."

"For Luther the sinner's experience of the terror of death is the real death. Actual physical death, even though sorrowful enough for loved ones, was in and of itself a much less serious matter ... The experience of the very presence of death is the real thing. [The individual] finally is 'frightened to death.'"[2]

This description fits the clinical model. When an OCD sufferer employs ERP successfully, she is, in a way, frightened to death, and then raised up into a state of assurance.

The final points of the Heidelberg Disputation deal with the crucial role of faith in righteousness and justification. Luther had touched on this subject in his *Lectures on Romans*, but at that time he inseparably linked faith to accusing oneself. Now, Luther has come to an entirely new understanding of faith. It is simply the assurance that God has declared us righteous; and like righteousness itself, it is a gift.

"Man believes with his heart and so is justified ... Grace says, 'believe in this,' and everything is already done."

This is as far as the lessons Luther learned from OCD took him. His first cure taught him the futility of works, and caused temporary relief from his symptoms. His second cure taught him about grace and faith and gained him permanent relief. The second cure was superior to the first in the sense that the strategy of willingly suffering fear can be applied to all types of obsessional fears, while accusing yourself (even though a great application of ERP) is more limited in scope.

Although by now, the spring of 1518, Luther was convinced that justification is by grace through faith, there were still strings attached. The gift of righteousness from God was not yet a free gift in one sense: A certain amount of despair and suffering, as Luther describes it in the Heidelberg Disputation, was still necessary before the gift of righteousness was given.

THE GOD OF MERCY

Not long after the Heidelberg Disputation, Luther made yet another great theological discovery. It was the realization that suffering is not necessary for justification. God declares people righteous simply when they hear the word of the Bible, and are drawn by God to believe it.

With this final discovery, Luther had in hand his famous doctrine of justification: "We are justified by grace alone through faith alone." Luther would insist throughout his life that this is the most important of all Christian doctrines. He writes in his *Lectures on Galatians* of 1535, "If we lose the doctrine of justification, we lose simply everything. Hence the most necessary and important thing is that we teach and repeat this doctrine daily."[3]

Luther's insight about God's mercy is considered so important that it is sometimes called in itself "the Reformation discovery." It happened in the same way as most of his great theological discoveries—through close study of the Bible. His focus in this instance was on St. Paul's letters. Approaching the text, Luther thought he already knew what the Apostle meant when he used the word "righteousness." Indeed, he had been preoccupied about what the Bible said about righteousness for nearly a decade. But now he saw something fresh.

Luther describes this discovery in two places. The most well-known is an autobiographical piece he wrote in 1545, just a year before his death. In *Preface to Latin Writings*, Luther

reviews the events that led up to the Reformation. He begins
with a discussion of the indulgence controversy of 1517. Then
he shares his experiences over the next two years, including his
interactions with the Pope and other key figures of the Reformation. Fascinatingly, he ends his preface with a vivid description of an event that occurred one night as he was studying
in the tower of his monastery. This was the moment when a
completely new understanding of the word righteousness was
revealed to him.

> "I hated that word 'righteousness of God,' which,
> according to the use and custom of all the teachers,
> I had been taught to understand philosophically re-
> garding the formal or active righteousness, as they
> called it, with which God is righteous and punishes
> the unrighteous sinner.
>
> Though I lived as a monk without reproach, I felt that
> I was a sinner before God with an extremely disturbed
> conscience ... At last, by the mercy of God, meditat-
> ing day and night, [I] began to understand that the
> righteousness of God is that by which the righteous
> lives by a gift of God, namely by faith ... Here I felt
> that I was altogether born again and had entered par-
> adise itself through open gates."[4]

In 1532, Luther provided another, briefer description of his
tower experience. Here he stresses even more clearly the role
of God's great mercy in declaring us righteous, and he also explains what caused him to experience this new insight.

> "[W]hen by God's grace I pondered, in the tower and
> heated room ... I soon came to the conclusion that if

we, as righteous men, ought to live from faith and if the righteousness of God contribute to the salvation of all who believe, then salvation won't be our merit but God's mercy. My spirit was thereby cheered. For it's by the righteousness of God that we're justified and saved through Christ. These words, which had before terrified me, now became more pleasing to me. The Holy Spirit unveiled the Scriptures for me in this tower."[5]

A sudden revelation into the meaning of scripture transported Luther into "paradise itself through open gates." He grasped a new meaning of the word righteous that revealed a new understanding of God: He is not a righteous God who punishes sinners, but rather a mercy-filled God who freely shares his own righteousness. As put by Brecht, "The gospel now says that the God of righteousness is the God of mercy."[6]

Returning to the clinical perspective, it is clear that Luther's insight into the greatness of God's mercy occurred in a somewhat different manner than his previous insights about works, grace, and faith. This was not a conclusion that he drew directly through overcoming his obsessional fears. Indeed, his OCD was already cured by then. Luther himself explains that his new understanding occurred because "the Holy Spirit unveiled the Scriptures."

One can still argue, however, that overcoming his obsessions paved the way for Luther's great insight in the tower. Once freed from his obsessional fears about his righteousness, he was able to study what the Bible said about righteousness with a clear mind unfettered from fear. This is no small matter. Severe obsessions become so strong that they destroy a person's ability to reason clearly about them. I have treated OCD sufferers so afraid of the topics of their fears that they could not bear to even read about them.

All of Luther's leading biographers agree that after his tower experience, his spiritual trials were cured. For instance, Bernhard Lohse writes, "The Reformation discovery concerns not only an exegetical but also an existential question: It decisively aided Luther in his personal inner conflicts, or anfechtungen."[7] And Brecht observes that as a result of Luther's Reformation discovery "the anfechtung subsided ... an enormous burden had been removed."[8] The clinical view, as has been previously noted, reverses the timing of the two events: It suggests Luther's anfechtung subsided first, when he cured his fears through willingly suffering his cross of fear; after that, he was able to make the Reformation discovery.

Here I Stand

After Luther's discoveries about grace, faith, and the meaning of righteousness, his personality seemed to undergo a transformation. Rather than harboring any sort of uncertainties, Luther was brimming with confidence at the Leipzig debate in 1519. A witness describes him: "He is affable and friendly, and in no sense dour or arrogant. He is equal to anything. In company he is vivacious, jocose, always cheerful and gay no matter how hard his adversaries press him."[9]

Events moved fast. In 1519, Luther launched wholeheartedly into leading the Reformation movement, and entered into a decade of some of the most energetic and productive years ever lived by anyone. In 1520, Luther published two books that would become among his best known: *The Babylonian Captivity*, which explains his thinking about how Catholic dogma imprisons the faithful, and *The Freedom of a Christian*, describing the joy he ascribes to a person liberated from Catholic teachings. Luther skewered his Church in these writings, going so far as to refute five of its seven sacred sacraments,[10] the essential rites by which people receive grace, and to deny any special role whatsoever for priests.

Not surprisingly, these attacks eventually caused Luther to be tried as a heretic. And it was his performance at an imperial assembly of the Holy Roman Empire in 1521 that cemented Luther's reputation as the greatest hero of Protestantism. Facing a tribunal ready to sentence him to burn at the stake unless he recanted, he stood strong in his beliefs for days on end. When offered a final chance, he finished with the words that have become his most famous.

> "I cannot and will not recant anything, since it is neither safe nor right to go against conscience. I cannot do otherwise, here I stand, may God help me, Amen."[11]

After he spoke them, Luther escaped martyrdom only with the help of his patron prince, Frederick the Wise, governor of Saxony, who had him spirited away and hidden in a castle for six months. After the trial at Worms, no compromise between Luther's followers and the Catholic Church was possible; the bloody Reformation wars soon began.

Appendix *A*

WHAT CAUSES OCD?

*T*o start, it must be emphasized that obsessive-compulsive disorder is a bona fide medical illness—a proven biological disorder of a bodily system, namely, the fear system of the brain. It is not caused by mental weakness, hang-ups, or unconscious conflicts. Hundreds of published research studies demonstrate beyond a doubt that OCD is irrefutably linked to specific chemical changes in the brain. Among these, studies of neurotransmitters, molecules that serve as messengers between brain cells, reveal that one called serotonin is abnormally active in OCD. When concentrations of serotonin are altered by medication, the severity of the disorder changes dramatically. Even more impressive are the findings from advanced imaging techniques such as functional magnetic resonance imaging (fMRI) and positron emission tomography (PET), which consistently reveal abnormally increased activity in specific regions of the brains of OCD sufferers, including the prefrontal and premotor cortex, the basal ganglia, and the amygdala. Aberrations are apparent at rest, and increase when patients are exposed to situations that intensify their obsessional fears. Furthermore, these abnormalities lessen and may even disappear with effective treatment.

Also supporting the biological nature of OCD are its proven causes. Trauma, strokes, infections, and autoimmune processes can all cause a person to suddenly develop typical obsessions and compulsions. Most commonly, genetic factors appear to provide the biologic basis for OCD. A large number of family and twin studies suggest that heredity accounts for 50 to 60 percent of the disorder's occurrence. It's worth noting that research supporting the physiological, biochemical nature of OCD is so robust that the US Congress has included it along with only a few other psychiatric disorders in the Mental Health Equitable Treatment Act. Doing so officially recognized OCD as a medical problem as real as diabetes or heart disease, and therefore equally deserving of coverage under insurance.

It is also true, however, that psychological factors play a major role in OCD's occurrence. This should not be surprising, as psychological factors are prominent in many common medical conditions. High blood pressure, for instance, is directly caused by the abnormal release of regulatory substances affecting blood flow. Yet hypertension has also been shown to be strongly related to psychological stress, and even to a certain style of personality (type A). What appears to happen in the majority of cases of OCD (as also with hypertension) is that genetic factors serve to make a person vulnerable, and psychological factors determine whether a full-blown case develops.

Much could be said about the biological and psychological factors involved in OCD. Our goal here will be limited to setting out a simple model that allows a person to make sense of OCD's puzzling symptoms. In this regard, biomedical research is not particularly enlightening. A few easily understood findings in the area of clinical psychology, however, explain a great deal.

The first finding is this: All obsessional thoughts are normal in themselves. Experiencing ideas, images, and urges of all possible types—including those that one would never want to think—is a normal part of the human condition. The brain generates such thoughts automatically. The basic normality of obsessional thoughts is critical to emphasize, because for half a century, psychiatrists insisted that obsessions resulted from pathological unconscious conflicts. Because of this misunderstanding, an enormous amount of useless psychotherapy was performed. In 1978, however, psychologist Stanley Rachman of the University of British Columbia undertook a landmark study.[1] He asked 124 students, hospital workers, and nurses: "Do you ever have thoughts or impulses that are intrusive and unacceptable?" Fully 80 percent answered that they did, at least once a week. Dr. Rachman and his coworkers then transcribed these "unacceptable thoughts" and placed them alongside the obsessions of OCD patients. The experts could not tell the difference between the unacceptable thoughts of average people and the obsessions of individuals afflicted with the disorder. The plain fact is: Most people routinely experience thoughts that are exactly the same in content as clinical obsessions. The only difference is how strong they are, and how frequently they occur.

The second important finding is that, as first put by Oxford psychologist Paul Salkovskis in 1989, OCD sufferers feel "an excessive sense of personal responsibility for preventing harm to self or others."[2] According to Salkovskis theory, a potentially upsetting thought causes no emotional reaction when it first comes into the mind. Indeed, if a person regards it as simply a piece of mental flotsam—an idea of little or no importance—then the thought will drift by without a ripple. But what happens with OCD sufferers is that they appraise a thought that others would ignore—a split-second evaluation that is not in full awareness—and conclude, as Salkovskis puts it, "that they might be responsible for harm to themselves or others unless they take action to prevent it." All of a sudden, an alarm sounds: "I better pay attention to that thought!" Now the thought will not float by. It must be dealt with.

Salkovskis theory explains why OCD sufferers never obsess about purely chance events, such as being caught in an earthquake or a hurricane. It is because they play no role in the occurrence or the prevention of such happenings. They have no degree of personal responsibility for the outcome. Obsessionals, on the other hand, readily develop symptoms when they are put into situations where they perceive that obvious harm may occur as a result of their actions. A striking example is the frequent onset of obsessions and compulsions in women immediately after the birth of a first child. Approximately 20 percent of all females with obsessive-compulsive disorder suffer its onset (almost always related to the safety of their babies) at this time of an enormous assumption of personal responsibility.

Studies suggest that taking excessive personal responsibility for harm is a deeply engrained personality trait. In one interesting study, Edna Foa of the University of Pennsylvania, a longtime leader in research in anxiety disorders, compared the responses of OCD sufferers, phobics, and a "normal" control group to differing levels of imagined danger: situations of high risk ("You see that a person sitting alone in a diner is choking"), medium risk ("You see some nails on a road"), and no significant risk ("You see a piece of string on the ground"). In the last two situations, OCD patients felt much more responsible for the outcome than did their phobic and "normal" counterparts, reporting more anxiety and more urges to check and make sure that harm would not occur.[3]

The degree of responsibility OCD sufferers take for preventing harm, as one might guess, is greatly magnified when they are alone. For instance, in a study from the University of British Columbia a group of people with contamination obsessions were asked to touch a toilet seat and then refrain from washing. They were to perform the task alone, then in the presence of an examiner. Obsessive-compulsives experienced much less anxiety and fewer urges to perform compulsions when another person was present—that is, when they felt less individual responsibility for the outcome.[4]

The third finding that helps make sense of OCD's puzzling symptoms is a curious feature in the way the brain processes fearful thoughts: Trying not to think a thought only makes a person think it even more. This nasty trick of the mind is self-evident and has also been proven experimentally. In 1987, psychologist Daniel Wegner of Trinity University in Texas performed a study entitled, "Paradoxical effects of thought suppression." Student volunteers were separated into two groups. One group heard a talk about white bears, the other was told not to think about white bears. The result: The group told not to think about the bears had bear thoughts throughout the day, while the other group rapidly forgot about them.[5] At some point, OCD sufferers almost always fall into this trap. They try to push an obsessional thought out of mind, and an ill-fated battle ensues as the thought becomes stronger.

In a similar manner, repeating an act again and again in response to an obsessional thought makes you think it even more. Consider the poor person with OCD. She tries to do something good to address a reasonable matter, like washing her hands because they are dirty. If she washes too much, however, she will become even more concerned about her hands; because the performance of compulsions makes obsessions stronger. Even worse, as obsessional fears grow stronger, they tend to become more *believable*. In my opinion, this is what makes obsessions so difficult to make sense of. Everyone knows that some people worry too much. But few can comprehend how a smart, reliable individual can buy into a totally unreasonable fear.

To sum up, here is a simple four-step model for the development of OCD.

1. An idea, image, or urge that triggers a sense of personal responsibility for harm enters the mind and becomes the focus of attention. Normal so far.

2. The thought is not dismissed from conscious awareness after appropriate action is taken to address it. Instead, it lingers. Still basically within normal limits, but this is the moment of truth.

3. If the individual now attempts to force the thought from mind, she falls into the white-bear trap. The thought is likely to become an obsession.

4. If she begins to repeat actions over and over in attempts to address and put right the fearful thought (i.e., develops compulsions), full-blown OCD will develop.

Appendix *B*

THE DSM-5-TR DIAGNOSTIC CRITERIA FOR OCD

*S*ince 1952, the American Psychiatric Association's *Diagnostic and Statistical Manual of Mental Disorders* has been the official manual for diagnosing mental disorders in the United States. It provides the specific criteria that are used in clinics and hospitals to diagnose various mental disorders. Treatment recommendations, as well as payment by health care providers, are often determined by DSM classifications.

The most recent edition of the *Diagnostic and Statistical Manual*, the *DSM-5-TR*, is a minor update of 2013's DSM-5. The DSM-5 itself was a significant revision of the previous manual. Modifications were made in the criteria used to identify a number of disorders, and a few new disorders were added. An important change was made in the classification of OCD. It was removed from the category of anxiety disorders, and put in a separate category. OCD's diagnostic criteria were also somewhat broadened to include cases that would not have been diagnosed as OCD in the past. A number of noted OCD researchers did not agree with these changes. I think that removing OCD from the category of anxiety disorders was a mistake, because OCD has always been categorized as such, and, after all, OCD is first and foremost a disorder of fearful thoughts.

According to the *DSM-5-TR*, obsessive-compulsive disorder is diagnosed when the following criteria are met:

A. Presence of obsessions, compulsions, or both:

Obsessions are defined by (1) and (2)

1. Recurrent and persistent thoughts, urges, or images that are experienced, at some time during the disturbance, as intrusive and unwanted; and that in most individuals cause marked anxiety or distress.

2. The individual attempts to ignore or suppress such thoughts, urges, or images, or to neutralize them with some other thought or action (i.e., by performing a compulsion).

Compulsions are defined by (1) and (2)

1. Repetitive behaviors (e.g., hand washing, ordering, checking) or mental acts (e.g., praying, counting, repeating words silently) that the individual feels driven to perform in response to an obsession or according to rules that must be applied rigidly.

2. The behaviors or mental acts are aimed at preventing or reducing anxiety or distress, or preventing some dreaded event or situation; however these behaviors or mental acts are not connected in a realistic way with what they are designed to neutralize or prevent, or are clearly excessive. Note: Young children may not be able to articulate the aims of these behaviors or mental acts.

B. The obsessions or compulsions are time-consuming (e.g., take more than 1 hour per day) or cause clinically significant distress or impairment in social, occupational, or other important areas of functioning.

C. The obsessive-compulsive symptoms are not attributable to the physiological effects of a substance (e.g., a drug of abuse or a medication) or another medical condition.

D. The disturbance is not better explained by the symptoms of another mental disorder (e.g., excessive worries, as in generalized anxiety disorder; preoccupation with appearance, as in body dysmorphic disorder; difficulty discarding or parting with possessions, as in hoarding disorder; hair pulling, as in trichotillomania [hair pulling disorder]; skin picking, as in excoriation [skin picking] disorder; stereotypies, as in stereotypic movement disorder; ritualized eating behavior, as in eating disorders; preoccupation with substances or gambling, as in substance-related and addictive disorders; preoccupations with having an illness, as in illness anxiety disorder; sexual urges or fantasies, as in paraphilic disorders; impulses, as in disruptive, impulse-control, and conduct disorders; guilty ruminations, as in major depressive disorder; thoughts insertion or delusional preoccupations, as in schizophrenia spectrum and other psychiatric disorders; or repetitive patterns of behavior, as in autism spectrum disorder).[1]

Appendix *C*

DR. MEYER'S DARING EXPERIMENT

*E*nglish psychologist Victor Meyer was one of the great pioneering behavioral therapy researchers of the twentieth century. After performing successful studies in the 1950s on the treatment of phobias with exposure and response prevention, he took on the treatment of obsessional fears in the 1960s. At that time, psychoanalysts believed that exposing people directly to their obsessional fears could overwhelm a person's unconscious defense mechanisms. Like a dam bursting, this could lead to a complete psychological breakdown. But Meyer was brave (he was a pilot and a prisoner of war in World War II), and he had the courage to proceed with what was seen at the time as a dangerous experiment. He exposed his obsessional patients directly and forcefully to their fears.

The following is Meyer's fascinating 1965 pilot study on the use of ERP in the treatment of OCD. It involved only two patients, but both had extraordinary histories of failed treatments. It shattered a host of long-standing and erroneous assumptions about the nature and treatment of obsessional fears, and set the stage for a flood of studies that proved beyond a doubt that ERP is a remarkably effective treatment for OCD.

Dr. Meyer's experiment. Meyer hospitalized two individuals with severe obsessive-compulsive disorder. Prior to their hospitalizations, both agreed to the challenging treatment techniques that would be employed. Both had extraordinarily difficult cases of what appeared to be treatment-resistant OCD. The first had been hospitalized three times previously for her disorder, and had tried medications, psychotherapy, and electroconvulsive therapy. The second had received eleven years of psychoanalysis, medications, electroconvulsive therapy, and even a prefrontal lobotomy for her disorder. No treatment had significantly helped either person. The first patient is described in this manner.

> "A 33-yr-old, intelligent school-mistress, married with one child and with a three-year history of severely disabling washing and cleaning rituals. After the birth of the child she started to worry about anything which might be 'dirty.' A wide range of objects and situations, e.g. door knobs, blankets, clothes, dustbins, meat, animals, men, sexual intercourse, were considered as 'contaminated by dirt' and led to almost continuous washing and cleaning."

The second patient is described as a "43-year-old woman of superior intellect." Her case is somewhat more complicated. Dr. Meyer reports,

> "She recalls that at the age of 10, after hearing a passage from the Bible 'to blaspheme against the Holy Ghost is unforgivable,' she became preoccupied with

this thought. Shortly afterwards, words like 'damn', 'blast', 'bloody' came to her mind despite all her attempts to resist them. By the age of 13, these intrusive thoughts centered on the idea of having sexual intercourse with the Holy Ghost. [Recent] ritualistic behaviour was evoked by any activity with sexual meaning, e.g. cleaning a pipe, putting on stockings, eating oblong objects, stepping on patterns in the shape of sex organs, entering underground trains etc. Her life had become a 'misery'. It took her hours to dress or to travel short distances."

Both patients were hospitalized for approximately five weeks. The essentials of therapy were the following. From the start, every effort was made to completely eliminate the performance of compulsions, including repeated acts of washing, cleaning, or any other activity. "Persuasion, reassurance, encouragement, and even bribery were employed." In addition, Dr. Meyer visited both patients daily for intensive ERP therapy sessions. In these visits, he made them confront their fears directly and continuously for lengthy periods of time. The first patient was required to perform tasks such as touching door knobs, handling her child's toys, and using public transport. The second patient's assignments included cleaning a smoking pipe, swearing out loud, eating sausages, and imagining herself having intercourse with the Holy Ghost.

Both patients improved dramatically within two months, and improvement remained one to two years later. In the case of Patient 1, excessive washing was almost entirely eliminated. Patient 2 reported that thoughts about the Holy Ghost and swear words only occasionally elicited rituals. Traveling presented almost no difficulties. She had obtained a teaching position, and had recently been promoted.[1]

To review Meyer's therapeutic strategy: When possible, he directed his patients to expose themselves to their obsessional fears by immersing themselves in a variety of real-life tasks that triggered them. For instance, the patient with contamination fears was directed to repeatedly touch doorknobs that she thought might harbor germs. The doctor's second patient, however, presented a special problem. How could he most forcefully expose her to the ghastly thought of having intercourse with the Holy Ghost? He came up with a brilliant solution. He directed her to purposefully imagine the situation. This is called imaginal exposure, and it has become a mainstay of ERP therapy in the present day.

In addition to employing both real-life and imaginal exposures, Meyer imposed strict response prevention. Because his patients were housed on a specialized unit, staff were able to assist them in recognizing and stopping compulsive behaviors twenty-four hours a day. Preventing compulsions is often the major stumbling block in ERP therapy. This round-the-clock attention was probably an important reason why the results of Meyer's study were so striking.

Since the 1970s, strategies for implementing ERP have been refined and improved. Fortunately, successful therapy does not require hospitalization. Outpatient therapy sessions with gradual and tolerable exposures work well, as long as patient motivation remains high. Often two or three months of weekly therapist visits, with daily ERP assignments carried out at home, are enough to produce a dramatic decrease in OCD symptoms.

NOTES

CHAPTER 1

1 Theodore Besterman, *A World Bibliography of Bibliographies and of Bibliographical Catalogues, Calendars, Abstracts, Digests, Indexes and the Like* (Rowman and Littlefield, 1963).

2 Heiko A. Oberman, *Luther: Man between God and the Devil*, trans. Eileen Walliser-Schwarzbart (New York: Image, 1992), 154.

3 Martin Luther, *Luther's Works*, ed. Helmut T. Lehman, Jaroslav Pelikan (St. Louis, MO: Concordia Publishing House, 1955-1986), 31:129 (hereafter cited as *LW*).

4 See Robert Herndon Fife, *The Revolt of Martin Luther* (New York: Columbia University Press, 1957), 93; Eric Gritsch, *Martin—God's Court Jester: Luther in Retrospect* (Philadelphia: Fortress, 1983), 205.

5 Ignaz von Döllinger, quoted in Gritsch, *Martin—God's Court Jester*, 204.

6 Hartmen Grisar, quoted in Gritsch, *Martin—God's Court Jester*, 205.

7 Paul Reiter, *Luther's Umwelt, Charakter und Psychose* (Copenhagen: Levin & Munksgaard, 1841), quoted in Erik H. Erikson, *Young Man Luther: A Study in Psychoanalysis and History* (New York: W. W. Norton, 1962), 27.

8 Erik Erikson, *Young Man Luther* (Norton Library Edition, 1962), 148.

9   Roland H. Bainton, *Here I Stand: A Life of Martin Luther* (New York: Meridian, 1995), 42.

10 We will use "cure" in the sense of relieving symptoms to the point where they no longer interfere into a person's life. Luther did have significant recurrences of obsessional thinking during several severe depressive spells in his later years.

11 *LW* 54:50, 73.

CHAPTER 2

1   Lyndal Roper, *Witch Craze: Terror and Fantasy in Baroque Germany* (London: Yale University Press, 2004)

2   Ladislas Orsy, *The Evolving Church and the Sacrament of Penance* (Denville, NJ: Dimension Books, 1982), 128.

3   Thomas N. Tentler, *Sin and Confession on the Eve of the Reformation* (Princeton, NJ: Princeton University Press, 1977), 135.

4   Pope Innocent III, considered one of the greatest popes of the Middle Ages, convened the Fourth Lateran Council, named after the church in Rome where the gathering took place. It was attended by more than 1,200 ecclesiastical representatives, and is one of the most important meetings in the history of the Roman Catholic Church. In addition to the ruling on confession, other doctrines approved by the Council included the creation of the Inquisition and the call for a crusade against Islam.

5   William of Auvergne, quoted in Peter Biller and A. J. Minnis, eds., *Handling Sin: Confession in the Middle Ages* (Rochester, NY: York Medieval Press, 1998), 96.

6   Tentler, *Sin and Confession*, 103.

7   Luther's confessor, Dr. Staupitz, told him, "Look here, if you expect Christ to forgive you, come in with something to forgive—parricide, blasphemy, adultery—instead of these scruples." (quoted in Bainton, *Here I Stand*, 40)

8   Orsy: personal communication (April, 2000).

9   Historian J. Jerome, writing in the French review *La Vie Spirituelle*, observes that there is "no mention of scruples in the annals of Moral Theology, until the end of the Middle Ages." Quoted by Father Thomas Santa, a Liguorian priest and editor of the magazine

Scrupulous Anonymous, on page 1 in the December 1998 issue.(Father Santa, an expert on the history of scruples in the Catholic Church, also made this point in a personal commumication to me.)

CHAPTER 3

1 See Fife, *The Revolt of Martin Luther*, 4-6.

2 Fife, *The Revolt of Martin Luther*, 6. Luther's good friend Philip Melanchthon knew Margarete well and spoke of her glowingly. He specifically mentions these traits.

3 *LW* 54:157, 235.

4 For instance, Luther said of his father, "All I am and have I owe to him." [source? – Emery] When Martin became a priest, his father rounded up twenty people and rode to the monastery to celebrate the occasion.

5 Bainton, *Here I Stand*, 22; quoted in Bainton, *Here I Stand*, 25.

6 Bainton, *Here I Stand*, 20.

7 Quoted in Richard Friedenthal, *Luther: His Life and Times*, trans. John Nowell (New York: Harcourt Brace Jovanovich, 1970), 13.

8 Martin Brecht, *Martin Luther: His Road to the Reformation, 1483–1521*, trans. James L. Schaaf (Minneapolis, MN: Fortress Press, 1993), 34.

9 Quoted in Brecht, *Martin Luther*, 47.

10 Quoted in Brecht, *Martin Luther*, 47.

11 Brecht, *Martin Luther*, 47, 69.

12 Quoted in Bainton, *Here I Stand*, 25.

13 *LW* 54:338, 24:259.

14 *LW* 48:332.

15 *LW* 44:387.

16 *LW* 4:341.

17 Luther says on several occasions that he spent fifteen years as a monk, from 1505–1520. 1520 was when he received the bull from the Pope threatening excommunication. He didn't cast off his cowl until 1523.

CHAPTER 4

1 The term "clinically significant" refers in a general sense to a problem that is of sufficient severity as to require treatment.

2 John Dillenberger, introduction to *Martin Luther: Selections from His Writings*, Martin Luther, ed. John Dillenberger (New York: Anchor, 1962), xvi; Bainton, *Here I Stand*, 42; Rudolf Thiel, *Luther: An Authentic Life Story* (Philadelphia: Muhlenberg Press, 1955), 99; Friedenthal, *Luther: His Life and Times*, 13.

3 Bainton, *Here I Stand*, 45.

4 Luther wrote five or six commentaries on Galatians. These quotes are from one written in 1535, which is the most famous. It is found in LW Vol 27.

5 Quoted in Fife, *The Revolt of Martin Luther*, 123.

6 *LW* 31:143.

7 *LW* 26:68.

8 Quoted in Oberman, *Luther*, 128.

9 *LW* 54:104.

10 *LW* 5:158.

11 *LW* 40:241.

12 *LW* 54:76.

13 *LW* 12:370.

14 See Bainton, *Here I Stand*, 41; Brecht, *Martin Luther*, 68; Erikson, *Young Martin Luther*, 155.

15 *LW* 54:94.

16 *LW* 54:15.

17 Quoted in Bainton, *Here I Stand*, 41.

18 See Erikson, *Young Martin Luther*, 156.

19 *LW* 5:271, 8:173.

20 *LW* 54:339, quoted in Bainton, *Here I Stand*, 34.

21 *LW* 28:81, 5:271.

22 *LW* 12:317.

23 *LW* 5:271, 12:315.

24 *LW* 24:24, quoted in Fife, *The Revolt of Martin Luther*, 92.

25 Brecht, *Martin Luther*, 70. "It is obvious how over the course of a few years a crisis developed in which the limits of this pious activity became evident in almost every aspect of his monastic life—the canonical hours, the fasts, and the confessional; through these means Luther could not come to the certainty he considered necessary . . . here, Luther's inmost identity was at stake . . . he devoted himself to a persistent search for a way out."

CHAPTER 5

1 Sigmund Freud, *Inhibitions, Symptoms, and Anxiety*, in *The Standard Edition of the Complete Psychological Works of Sigmund Freud*, ed. J. Strachey et al. (London: Hogarth Press, 1959), 20:113. Freud published fourteen major papers on obsessive-compulsive disorder, more than on any other topic he wrote on.

2 Quoted in Edna Foa, "Behavioral Treatment of Obsessive-Compulsive Patients," *Highland Highlights* 13, no. 1 (1990): 25.

3 For example, cognitive behavioral therapy, mindfulness, and acceptance and commitment therapy.

4 Jonathan Grayson, *Freedom from Obsessive-Compulsive Disorder: A Personalized Recovery Program for Dealing with Uncertainty* (New York: Berkley Books, 2014), 60: "There are, in fact, no conclusive studies of successful OCD treatment programs that do not include exposure and response prevention in some form."

5 Staupitz was a high-ranking member of the Augustinian Order of monks, the vicar general of twenty-seven monasteries. Early on, he recognized Luther's potential as an academic and took Luther under his wing. He played a critical role in Luther's life, providing him with invaluable support and advice during his most difficult times. In Luther's later years, Staupitz remained the only Catholic priest he continued to greatly admire and respect.

6 Bainton, *Here I Stand*, 45.

7 *LW* 35:254.

8 *LW* 54:46.

9 Bainton, *Here I Stand*, 40.

10 Brecht, *Martin Luther*, 132.

11 *LW* 10:236.

12 *LW* 10:238, 32.

13 *LW* 14:151. Quote is from Luther's exegesis of the phrase in Psalm 32, "I will confess my transgressions to the Lord," taken from his book, *The Seven Penitential Psalms*, which was an outgrowth of his first lectures on the Psalms and published in 1517.

14 *LW* 10:368.

15 Jonathan Abramowitz, *Getting Over OCD: A 10-Step Workbook for Taking Back Your Life* (New York: Guilford Press, 2018), 204.

16 Joseph W. Ciarrocchi, *The Doubting Disease: Help for Scrupulosity and Religious Obsessions* (Mahwah, NJ: Paulist Press, 1995), 83.

17 *LW* 10:243 .

18 *LW* 10:368

19 Brecht, *Martin Luther*, 76.

20 *LW* 10:371

21 Alistair McGrath, *Luther's Theology of the Cross: Martin Luther's Theological Breakthrough* (Oxford: Blackwell, 1990) 155.

22 Brecht, *Martin Luther*, 136.

CHAPTER 6

1 See Bernhard Lohse, *Martin Luther's Theology: Its Historical and Systemic Development*, ed. and trans. Roy A. Harrisville (Minneapolis, MN: Fortress, 1999), 75. "For Luther, 'to justify' and 'to declare as righteous,' are synonymous."

2 *LW* 25:252.

3 *LW* 54:50.

4 *LW* 54:73.

5 Quoted in Bainton, *Here I Stand*, 283.

6 This was the approach of a Roman Catholic Theologian named Gabriel Biel. He is credited, along with the English theologian William Occam (of Occam's razor fame), with developing a broad theological/philosophical view that was termed "Via Moderna." It is known that Luther studied Biel intensely, and it was the Via Moderna approach to righteousness that he learned in his early monastery years.

7 *LW* 31:68.

8 Quoted in Bainton, *Here I Stand*, 56.

9 *LW* 31:179.

10 Brecht, *Martin Luther*, 175.

11 *LW* 31:248.

CHAPTER 7

1 *LW* 54:19.

2 *LW* 35:366.

3 Quoted in Brecht, *Martin Luther*, 80.

4 *LW* 31:129.

5 *LW* 33:190.

6 Luther to Barbara Lisskirchen, April 30, 1531, in *Luther: Letters of Spiritual Counsel*, ed. and trans. Theodore G. Tappert (Vancouver, BC: Regent College Publishing, 2003), 115; Luther, table talk recorded by Caspar Heydenreich, February 18, 1542, in *Letters*, 133.

7 *LW* Vol. 5, 5:46

8 Luther, table talk recorded by Conrad Cordatus, autumn 1531, in *Letters*, 118.

9 Luther, table talk recorded by Conrad Cordatus, autumn 1532, in *Letters*, 122.

10 *LW* 5:48.

11 *LW* 3:171.

12 *LW* 7:308, 29:214.

CHAPTER 8

1 *LW* 40:349.

2 Johannes Tauler, "Sermon 40", in *Johannes Tauler Sermons*, trans. Maria Shrady (New York: Paulist Press, 1985), 143.

3 Tauler, "Sermon 59," in *Sermons*, 164.

4 Tauler, "Sermon 76," in *Sermons*, 172.

5 *LW* 48:36.

6 *LW* 26:372.

7 Martin Luther, "Psalm 22," in *Martin Luther's Commentary on the First Twenty-Two Psalms*, ed. and trans. Henry Cole (London, 1826) 4:387.

8 Luther, "Psalm 22," in *Commentary* 4:388.

9 Luther, "Psalm 6," in *Commentary* 1:307

10 Luther, "Psalm 6," in *Commentary* 1:310

11 Luther, "Psalm 5," in *Commentary* 1:244

12 *LW* 42:183.

CHAPTER 9

1 *LW* 31:39.

2 Gerhard O. Forde, *On Being a Theologian of the Cross: Reflections on Luther's Heidelberg Disputation, 1518* (Grand Rapids, MN: W. B. Eerdmans, 1997), 100, 103.

3 *LW* 26:26.

4 *LW* 34:337.

5 *LW* 54:194.

6 Brecht, *Martin Luther*, 226

7 Lohse, Martin Luther's Theology, 86.

8 Brecht, *Martin Luther*, 226, 227.

9 Bainton, *Here I Stand*, 87

10 The seven sacraments of the Roman Catholic Church are baptism, confirmation, eucharist, reconciliation, anointing of the sick, Holy Orders, and marriage.

11 *LW* 32:113.

APPENDIX A

1 Stanley Rachman and P. De Silva, "Abnormal and Normal Obsessions," *Behaviour Research and Therapy* 16, no. 4 (1978): 233–248.

2 Paul Salkovskis, "Cognitive-Behavioural Factors and the Persistence of Intrusive Thoughts in Obsessional Problems," *Behaviour Research and Therapy* 27, no. 6 (1989): 677–684.

3 Edna Foa et al., "Inflated Perception of Responsibility for Harm in Obsessive-Compulsive Disorder," *Journal of Anxiety Disorders* 15, no. 4 (2001): 259–275.

4 Roz Shafran, "The Manipulation of Responsibility in Obsessive-Compulsive Disorder," *British Journal of Clinical Psychology* 36, no. 3 (1997): 397–407.

5 David M. Wegner et al., "Paradoxical Effects of Thought Suppression," *Journal of Personality and Social Psychology* 53, no. 1 (1987): 5–13.

APPENDIX B

1 American Psychiatric Association, *Diagnostic and Statistical Manual of Mental Disorders: DSM 5.*, rev. ed. (Washington, DC: American Psychiatric Association, 2022), 235ff.

APPENDIX C

1 Victor Meyer, "Modification of Expectations in Cases with Obsessional Rituals," *Behaviour Research and Therapy* 4, no. 4 (1966): 273–80.

About the Author

*I*an Osborn, M.D. is an internationally known lecturer and author on the subject of obsessive-compulsive disorder with extensive experience treating OCD patients in both outpatient and and inpatient settings.

He has taught psychiatry on the faculties of the University of New Mexico and Penn State University, and served for a decade as chief of psychiatry and director of mental health at Centre Community Hospital in State College, Pa. His previous books include *Tormenting Thoughts and Secret Rituals: the Secret Epidemic of Obsessive-Compulsive Disorder*, and *Can Christianity Cure Obsessive-Compulsive Disorder? A Psychiatrist Explores the Role of Faith in Treatment.*

INDEX

Martin Luther, defense of, 3
Reformation, 1, 5, 51–52, 53, 54
works, good, 51

R

Reformation, Protestant. *see also*
Protestant Church
"Disputation on the Power and
Efficacy of Indulgences"/95
theses (1517), 51–52, 53, 54
Luther, Martin—obsessive-
compulsive disorder (OCD), 5
"Reformation discovery," 79, 82
righteousness, 1
"Reformation discovery," 79, 82
Reiter, Paul, 3
Renaissance
Bosch, Hieronymus, 8
bubonic plague, 7
hell & purgatory, 8
humanistic achievements, 7
Jerome, J., 11
La Vie Spirituelle, 11
moral theology, 8
obsessive-compulsive disorder
(OCD), 11–12
Orsy, Ladislas (priest), 8, 11
scruples/fears, 11–12
uprisings, 7
righteousness
Catholic Church, 1–2, 47, 51
Luther, Martin, 1–2, 4–5, 45,
47–48, 48–51, 75–81
Oberman, Heiko, 2

S

Satan, 60–61, 63
scholastic movement, 8–9
scruples/fears, 10–12, 30
self-abnegation, 31–32
spiritual trials, 2, 4, 5, 11, 26, 39,
48–49, 51
Staupitz, Johannes von (priest),
37–38, 39, 57–58

T

Tauler, Johannes (priest), 66–68
Tentler, Thomas, 9, 11
Tetzel, Johann, 52
"Theology of the Cross," 77–78
truth, 41–42, 48–49, 77

U

University at Erfurt, 16–17
University in Wittenberg,
Augustinian, 37–39

W

William of Auvergne, 10
witchcraft, 8, 14
works, good
Catholic Church, 1–2, 47, 49–50
Luther, Martin—beliefs, 42, 45,
47–50, 51, 76
Luther, Martin—obsessive-
compulsive disorder (OCD), 20,
28–29, 37, 39, 40, 45, 49, 58, 65
Protestant Church, 51

Y

Young Man Luther, 3

Made in the USA
Las Vegas, NV
20 August 2024

94173773R00080